First Workshop on Understanding Implicit and Underspecified Language (UNIMPLICIT 2021)

Held online due to COVID-19

Bangkok, Thailand
5 – 6 August 2021

ISBN: 978-1-7138-3389-5

Printed from e-media with permission by:

Curran Associates, Inc.
57 Morehouse Lane
Red Hook, NY 12571

CURRAN ASSOCIATES INC. proceedings.com

Some format issues inherent in the e-media version may also appear in this print version.

Association for Computational Linguistics
209 N. Eighth Street
Stroudsburg, Pennsylvania 18360

Phone: 1-570-476-8006
Fax: 1-570-476-0860

acl@aclweb.org

Additional copies of this publication are available from:

Curran Associates, Inc.
57 Morehouse Lane
Red Hook, NY 12571 USA
Phone: 845-758-0400
Fax: 845-758-2633
Email: curran@proceedings.com
Web: www.proceedings.com

UNIMPLICIT 2021

The First Workshop on Understanding Implicit and Underspecified Language

Proceedings of the Workshop

August 5-6, 2021
Bangkok, Thailand (online)

Introduction

Welcome to UnImplicit: The First Workshop on Understanding Implicit and Underspecified Language. The focus of this workshop is on implicit and underspecified phenomena in language, which pose serious challenges to standard natural language processing models as they often require incorporating greater context, using symbolic inference and common-sense reasoning, or more generally, going beyond strictly lexical and compositional meaning constructs. This challenge spans all phases of the NLP model's life cycle: from collecting and annotating relevant data, through devising computational methods for modelling such phenomena, to evaluating and designing proper evaluation metrics.

In this workshop, our goal is to bring together theoreticians and practitioners from the entire NLP cycle, from annotation and benchmarking to modeling and applications, and to provide an umbrella for the development, discussion and standardization of the study of understanding implicit and underspecified language.

The workshop includes a shared task on modeling the necessity of clarifications due to aspects of meaning that are implicit or underspecified in context. Two teams participated in the shared task and submitted results.

In total, we received 23 paper submissions (among them 12 extended abstracts and 3 shared task papers), out of which 20 were accepted. All accepted submissions are presented as posters, including two additional presentations of Finding papers accepted to the ACL main conference. The workshop also includes two invited talks on topics related to implicit language. The program committee consisted of 24 researchers, who we'd like to thank for providing helpful and constructive reviews on the papers. We'd also like to thank all authors for their submissions and interest in our workshop.

Michael, Reut and Yoav

Organizers

Michael Roth, Stuttgart University
Reut Tsarfaty, Bar-Ilan University
Yoav Goldberg, Bar-Ilan University and AI2

Program Committee

Omri Abend, Hebrew University of Jerusalem
Johan Bos, University of Groningen
Nancy Chang, Google
Vera Demberg, Saarland University
Katrin Erk, University of Texas at Austin
Annemarie Friedrich, Bosch Center for Artificial Intelligence
Dan Goldwasser, Purdue University
Yufang Hou, IBM Research Ireland
Ruihong Huang, Texas A&M University
Mirella Lapata, University of Edinburgh
Junyi Jessy Li, University of Texas at Austin
Ray Mooney, University of Texas at Austin
Philippe Muller, University of Toulouse
Vincent Ng, University of Texas at Dallas
Tim O'Gorman, University of Massachusetts Amherst
Karl Pichotta, Memorial Sloan Kettering Cancer Center
Massimo Poesio, Queen Mary University
Niko Schenk, Amazon
Nathan Schneider, Georgetown University
Vered Shwartz, Allen Institute for AI & University of Washington
Elior Sulem, University of Pennsylvania
Sara Tonelli, Fondazione Bruno Kessler
Ben Van Durme, Johns Hopkins University & Microsoft Semantic Machines
Luke Zettlemoyer, University of Washington & Facebook

Invited Speakers

Martha Palmer, University of Colorado at Boulder
Chris Potts, Stanford University

Table of Contents

Workshop Program

Thursday, August 5, 2021 [UTC+0]

14:50–16:00 **Talk session I**

14:50–15:00 ***Opening***

15:00–16:00 *Invited Talk: Martha Palmer*
Martha Palmer

16:00–17:00 **Poster session I**

16:00–17:00 *Let's be explicit about that: Distant supervision for implicit discourse relation classification via connective prediction*
Murathan Kurfalı and Robert Östling

16:00–17:00 *Implicit Phenomena in Short-answer Scoring Data*
Marie Bexte, Andrea Horbach and Torsten Zesch

16:00–17:00 *Evaluation Guidelines to Deal with Implicit Phenomena to Assess Factuality in Data-to-Text Generation*
Roy Eisenstadt and Michael Elhadad

16:00–17:00 *UnImplicit Shared Task Report: Detecting Clarification Requirements in Instructional Text*
Michael Roth and Talita Anthonio

16:00–17:00 ***Additional posters: Finding papers and extended abstracts***

Thursday, August 5, 2021 [UTC+0] (continued)

17:00–17:45 Discussion Session I

17:45–18:45 Poster session II

17:45–18:45 *Improvements and Extensions on Metaphor Detection*
Weicheng Ma, Ruibo Liu, Lili Wang and Soroush Vosoughi

17:45–18:45 *Human-Model Divergence in the Handling of Vagueness*
Elias Stengel-Eskin, Jimena Guallar-Blasco and Benjamin Van Durme

17:45–18:45 *A Mention-Based System for Revision Requirements Detection*
Ahmed Ruby, Christian Hardmeier and Sara Stymne

17:45–18:45 *TTCB System Description to a Shared Task on Implicit and Underspecified Language 2021*
Peratham Wiriyathammabhum

17:45–18:45 *Additional posters: Finding papers and extended abstracts*

18:45–19:45 Talk session II

18:45–19:45 *Invited Talk: Chris Potts*
Chris Potts

Thursday, August 5, 2021 [UTC+0] (continued)

19:45–20:30 Discussion session II

Let's be explicit about that: Distant supervision for implicit discourse relation classification via connective prediction

Murathan Kurfalı
Department of Linguistics
Stockholm University
Stockholm, Sweden
murathan.kurfali@ling.su.se

Robert Östling
Department of Linguistics
Stockholm University
Stockholm, Sweden
robert@ling.su.se

Abstract

In implicit discourse relation classification, we want to predict the relation between adjacent sentences in the absence of any overt discourse connectives. This is challenging even for humans, leading to shortage of annotated data, a fact that makes the task even more difficult for supervised machine learning approaches. In the current study, we perform implicit discourse relation classification without relying on any labeled implicit relation. We sidestep the lack of data through explicitation of implicit relations to reduce the task to two subproblems: language modeling and explicit discourse relation classification, a much easier problem. Our experimental results show that this method can even marginally outperform the state-of-the-art, in spite of being much simpler than alternative models of comparable performance. Moreover, we show that the achieved performance is robust across domains as suggested by the zero-shot experiments on a completely different domain. This indicates that recent advances in language modeling have made language models sufficiently good at capturing inter-sentence relations without the help of explicit discourse markers.

1 Introduction

Discourse relations describe the relationship between discourse units, e.g. clauses or sentences. These relations are either signalled explicitly with a discourse connective (e.g. *because*, *and*) or expressed implicitly and are inferred by sequential reading (Example 1 below).

(1) A figure above 50 indicates the economy is likely to expand. **[While]** One below 50 indicates a contraction may be ahead. *(Comparison - wsj_0233)*

The relations in the latter category are called *implicit discourse relations* and they are of special significance because their lack of an explicit signal makes them challenging to annotate for even humans, suggested by the lower inter-annotator agreements on implicit relations (Zeyrek and Kurfalı, 2017; Zikánová et al., 2019), let alone classify automatically.

Resources for implicit discourse relations, therefore, are very limited. Even the Penn Discourse Tree Bank 2.0 (PDTB 2.0) (Prasad et al., 2008), which is the most popular resource, includes merely 16K implicit discourse relations, all annotated on the same domain. Explicit discourse relations, on the other hand, are proven to be simple enough to be obtained both manually and automatically. Previous work shows that explicit relations in English have a low level of ambiguity, so the discourse relation can be classified with more than 94% accuracy from the discourse connective alone (Pitler and Nenkova, 2009). This has inspired others to predict connectives for the implicit discourse relations and add them as additional features to existing supervised classifiers (Zhou et al., 2010; Xu et al., 2012).

Our work takes this idea one step further by reducing the amount of supervision required. Instead of training a separate connective classifier, we generate a set of *candidate explicit relations* that are obtained by inserting explicit discourse markers between sentences and score the resulting segments using a large pre-trained language model.[1] The candidates are then classified with an accurate explicit discourse relation classifier, and the final implicit relation prediction can be obtained by either using the candidate with the highest-scoring connective, or marginalizing over the whole distribution of explicit connectives.

The main contributions of our papers are as follows:

[1] In the reminder of the paper, these candidate explicit relations are simply referred as *candidates*.

Proceedings of the 1st Workshop on Understanding Implicit and Underspecified Language (UnImplicit 2021), pages 1–10
Bangkok, Thailand (online), August 5, 2021.

- We show that this simple approach is very effective and even marginally outperforms the current state-of-the-art method that does not use labeled implicit discourse relation data, even though that method uses a significantly more complex adversarial domain adaptation model (Huang and Li, 2019).

- To the best of our knowledge, this is the first study to go beyond the default four-way classification under the low-resource scenario assumption where no labeled implicit discourse relation is available. We show that the proposed pipeline maintains its performance (relative to the baselines) in a more challenging 11-way classification as well as across domains (i.e., biomedical texts (Prasad et al., 2011)).

- We offer explicitation of implicit discourse relations as a probing task to evaluate language models. Despite their relevancy, discourse relations are mostly overlooked in the assessments of language models' understanding of context. As a secondary aim, we investigate a wide range of pre-trained language models' understanding of inter-sentential relations.

We hope that the proposed pipeline will be another step in overcoming the data-bottleneck problem in discourse studies.

2 Background

2.1 Implicit Discourse Relations

PDTB 2.0 adopts a lexicalized approach where each relation consists of a discourse connective (e.g. "but", "and") which acts as a predicate taking two arguments. For each relation, annotators were asked to annotate the connective, the two text spans that hold the relation and the sense it conveys based on the PDTB sense hierarchy (Prasad et al., 2008). The text span which is syntactically bound to the connective is called the second argument (arg2) whereas the other is the first argument (arg1). "Additionally, implicit relations are annotated with that explicit connective which according to judgements best expresses the sense of the relation."

However, in certain cases, a relation holds between the adjacent sentences despite the lack of an overt connective (see Example 1). PDTB 2.0 recognizes such relations as *implicit discourse relations*. Additionally, implicit relations are annotated with an explicit connective which best expresses the sense of the relation is according to annotators. The connective inserted by the annotators is termed as "*implicit connective*" (e.g. "while" in Example 1). Unlike explicit relations where there is an explicit textual cue (the connective), implicit relations can only be inferred which makes them more challenging to spot and annotate.

2.2 Related Work

The research on implicit discourse relation classification is overwhelmingly supervised (Pitler et al., 2009; Rutherford and Xue, 2015; Lan et al., 2017; Nie et al., 2019; Kim et al., 2020). Although unsupervised methods were present in the earliest attempts (Marcu and Echihabi, 2002), they haven't received serious attention and much research concentrated on increasing the available supervision to deal with the data; most prominently, either by automatically generating artificial data (Sporleder and Lascarides, 2008; Braud and Denis, 2014; Rutherford and Xue, 2015; Wu et al., 2016; Shi et al., 2017) or through introducing auxiliary but similar tasks to the training routine to leverage additional information (Zhou et al., 2010; Xu et al., 2012; Liu et al., 2016; Lan et al., 2017; Qin et al., 2017; Shi and Demberg, 2019a; Nie et al., 2019). Zhou et al. (2010) and Xu et al. (2012) constitute the earliest examples where the classification of implicit relations are assisted via connective prediction. Both studies employ language models to predict suitable connectives for implicit relations which are, then, either used as additional features or classified directly.

Ji et al. (2015) is one of the few recent distantly supervised[2] studies which tackle implicit relation classification as a domain adaptation problem where the labeled explicit relations are regarded as the source domain and the unlabeled implicit relations as the target. Huang and Li (2019) improves upon Ji et al. (2015) by employing adversarial domain adaption with a novel reconstruction component.

2.3 Pre-trained Language Models

BERT Bidirectional Encoder Representations for Transformers (BERT) is a multi-layer Transformer encoder based language model (Devlin

[2]Previous work uses the term *unsupervised* (domain adaptation). Although we use the same amount of supervision with earlier work (no labeled implicit relation are utilized), we believe *distant supervision* describes the method better.

et al., 2019). As opposed to directional models where the input is processed from one direction to another, the transformer encoder reads its input at once; hence, BERT learns word representations in full context (both from left and from right). BERT is trained with two pre-training objectives on large-scale unlabeled text: (i) Masked Language Modelling and (ii) Next Sentence Prediction.

A number of BERT variants are available that differ in terms of (i) their architecture, e.g. BERT-base (*12-layer, 110M parameters*) and BERT-large (*24-layer, 340M parameters*); (ii) whether the letter casing in its input is preserved (-cased) or not (-uncased); (iii) their masking strategy, e.g. word pieces (*default*) or whole words (-whole-word-masking).

RoBERTa RoBERTa (Liu et al., 2019) shares the same architecture as BERT but improves upon it via introducing a number of refinements to the training procedure, such as using more data with larger batch sizes, adopting a larger vocabulary, removal of the NSP objective and dynamic masking.

DistilBERT DistilBERT was introduced by (Sanh et al., 2019). It is created by applying knowledge distillation to BERT which is a compression technique in which a small model learns to mimic the full output distribution of the target model (in this case: BERT). DistilBERT is claimed to retain 97% of BERT performance despite being 40% smaller and 60% faster, as suggested by its performance on Question Answering task.

GPT-2 Generatively Pre-trained Transformer (GPT-2) is a unidirectional transformer based language model trained on a dataset of 40 GB of web crawling data (Radford et al., 2019). Unlike BERT, GPT-2 works like a traditional language model where each token can only attend to its previous context. GPT-2 has four variants which differ from each other in the number of layers, ranging from 12 (small) to 48 (XL).

3 Model

The proposed method consists of three main components: (i) a candidate generator that generates sentence pairs connected by each of a set of discourse connectives, (ii) a language model that estimates the likelihood of each candidate, and (iii) an explicit discourse relation classifier to be used on the candidates. Whole pipeline is shown in Figure 1. The proposed methodology does not require even a single implicit discourse relation annotation and is only distantly supervised where the supervision comes from the explicit discourse relations used in training the classifier.

The main motivation behind the proposed pipeline is the finding that discourse relations are easily classifiable if they are explicitly marked (Pitler and Nenkova, 2009). We further verify this finding via a preliminary experiment which showed that four-way classification could be performed with an F-score of 88.74 when the implicit discourse relations are "explicitated" with the *gold implicit connectives* they are annotated with (see Table 2). This finding is significant not only because it justifies our motivation but also shows the potential of the current approach. Secondarily, the task requires a high level understanding of the context which allows us to investigate the pre-trained language models capabilities in detecting inter-sentential relations.

3.1 Candidate Generation

Recall Example 1, which contains an implicit relation between argument 1 ("*A figure above ... to expand.*") and argument 2 ("*one below ... be ahead.*").

Given a list of English connectives (*and*, *because*, *but*, etc.), we generate the following explicit relation candidates for a given implicit relation:

A_1	C	A_2
... to expand	**and**	[o]ne below ...
... to expand	**because**	[o]ne below ...
... to expand	**but**	[o]ne below ...

The list of connectives are chosen among the lexical items PDTB 2.0 annotation guideline recognizes as discourse connectives (Prasad et al., 2008). Of the listed 100 connectives,[3] we limit ourselves to 65 one-word connectives to generate the candidates due to masked language models' inability to predict multiple tokens simultaneously.

3.2 Prediction of Implicit Connectives

Our next task is to produce a distribution over connectives C conditioned on the context (arguments A_1 and A_2). For unidirectional language models (in our case: GPT-2 variants), we estimate this by computing the language model likelihood of the entire candidates and normalizing over the connec-

[3]The modified connectives such as "partly because" are not counted as distinct types.

Model	4-Way	11-Way
PDTB train (Explicit)	13639	12695
PDTB test	1046	1040
BioDRB(test)	247	140
BioDRB(full)	3001	1755

Table 1: Number of instances in the respective datasets. For the BioDRB test and full distinctions, please refer to Section 5.3.

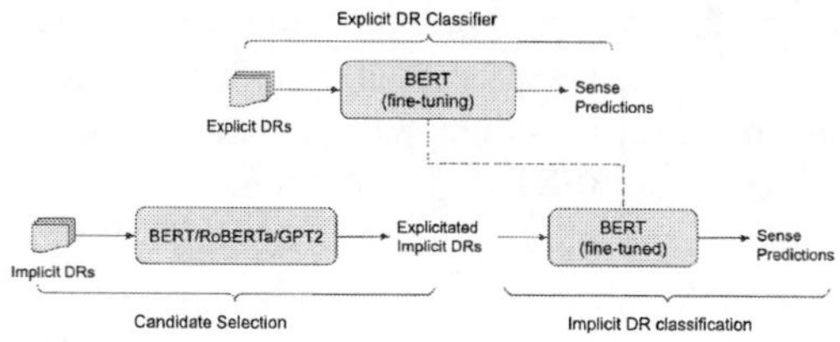

Figure 1: A high level visualization of the proposed pipeline.

tives:

$$P_{Conn}(C|A_1, A_2) \propto P_{LM}(A_1\ C\ A_2)$$

With bidirectional masked language models (in our case: DistilBERT, BERT and RoBERTa) we need to instead provide a candidate template by inserting the special sentence separation ([SEP]) and masking ([MASK]) tokens. Then it is simply a matter of normalizing over the model's estimated probability of the connective being inserted at the position of the masking token:

$$P_{Conn}(C|A_1, A_2) \propto P_{LM}(C|A_1\ [\text{SEP}]\ [\text{MASK}]\ A_2\ [\text{SEP}])$$

3.3 Explicit Discourse Relation Classifier

We regard discourse relation classification as a sentence pair classification task and build a classifier on top of the pre-trained BERT model from Devlin et al. (2019) using the recommended fine-tuning strategy. Specifically, the first and second arguments are separated via the special separator token ([SEP]) with the connective on the second argument and the [CLS] token is used for classification through a fully connected layer with softmax activation. This classifier gives us a model for the distribution $P_{Exp}(l|C, A_1, A_2)$ of relation labels l conditioned on the connective C and its arguments A_1 and A_2.

The annotation of explicit and implicit relations in the PDTB 2.0 differ in several aspects. In the case of implicit relations, PDTB 2.0 annotates arguments in the order they appear in the text, hence implicit relations can only manifest one configuration (i.e. arg1, [conn], arg2). On the other hand, the relative argument order of the explicit relations can vary to the extent that sometimes the arguments may interrupt each other (e.g. *Of course*, if **the film contained dialogue**, *Mr. Lane's Artist would be called a homeless person.* [from wsj-0039]). In order to remedy for this disparity to some extent, we only use the explicit relations which share the same relative argument order with implicit relations (i.e. arg1, conn, arg2) in training the classifier so that there is not any discrepancy in terms of the relation structure between training and inference phases. In total, 2558 (13.85%) explicit relations that do not follow the (arg1,conn,arg2) order are left out.

3.4 Final Model

In our experiments we combine the models in two ways. The simplest way is a straightforward pipeline approach, where the single most likely implicit connective is predicted, and then fed to the explicit relation classifier:

$$P(l|A_1, A_2) = P_{Exp}(l|\arg\max_C P_{Conn}(C|A_1, A_2), A_1, A_2)$$

Even though the level of ambiguity in English discourse connectives is relatively low, we also try to account for this ambiguity by marginalizing over all connectives:

$$P(l|A_1, A_2) = \sum_C P_{Exp}(l|C, A_1, A_2) \times P_{Conn}(C|A_1, A_2)$$

4 Experiments

We follow the experimental setting of Huang and Li (2019) which is originally adopted by (Ji et al., 2015). The implicit relations in the PDTB 2.0 sections 21-22 are allocated as the test set whereas the explicit relations in sections 2-20;23-24 are used as the training and 0-1 as the development set of the explicit relation classifier. The evaluation is performed for both the four first-level and the most common 11 second-level senses. For the former, we report both per-class and the macro-average F1-scores similar to Huang and Li (2019) whereas the accuracy is also reported on the second level

Model	Temp	Cont	Comp	Exp	4-way	11-way	
	F-score						Acc
Supervised	45.85	57.74	58.35	75.01	59.24	39.33	55.42
Gold Connective	77.29	96.23	88.01	93.42	88.74	57.56	78.87
Most Common Conn (but)	0.00	0.00	24.45	0.07	6.13	2.68	11.60
Most Common Sense	0.00	0.00	0.00	69.41	17.35	3.74	25.89
(Ji et al., 2015)	19.26	41.39	25.74	**68.08**	38.62	-	-
(Huang and Li, 2019)	**31.25**	48.04	25.15	59.15	40.90	-	-
BERT-base-uncased	14.97	29.06	32.05	59.45	33.88	13.88	23.16
+ Margin	19.49	36.54	32.48	52.99	35.37	14.12	24.45
BERT-large-cased	9.33	27.06	36.89	68.58	35.47	12.29	24.55
+ Margin	9.76	35.62	38.80	67.97	38.04	13.24	26.86
BERT-large-cased-wwm	10.89	36.29	42.69	62.38	38.06	16.79	27.23
+ Margin	15.02	41.97	41.81	60.80	39.90	17.50	28.74
BERT-large-uncased	25.69	30.55	30.10	62.50	37.21	15.57	25.25
+ Margin	27.32	41.01	32.28	59.07	39.92	15.67	28.01
BERT-large-uncased-wwm	18.35	35.20	40.19	58.88	38.15	16.47	26.80
+ Margin	17.27	42.93	41.16	55.61	39.24	17.26	29.17
DistilBERT-base-cased	16.77	46.19	23.19	39.07	31.31	15.87	22.71
+ Margin	21.09	**48.05**	29.25	37.04	33.86	16.68	26.38
RoBERTa-base	9.65	19.64	36.57	66.72	33.14	11.67	23.54
+ Margin	9.18	22.77	35.90	66.36	33.55	13.01	25.32
RoBERTa-large	10.79	30.32	48.35	68.44	39.48	16.15	27.66
+ Margin	13.30	33.19	**49.52**	67.90	40.98	17.63	29.57
GPT2	16.60	31.96	35.79	62.62	36.74	11.68	24.04
+ Margin	18.27	37.31	35.93	61.70	38.30	13.07	26.02
GPT2-large	19.91	35.27	40.38	59.17	38.68	15.18	25.63
+ Margin	23.17	40.55	40.30	60.39	**41.10**	16.03	27.50
GPT2-XL	21.59	30.88	40.18	63.01	38.92	16.98	26.01
+ Margin	23.06	34.49	42.66	63.98	41.05	18.50	28.32

Table 2: The results of the proposed methodology with various pre-trained language models. The average performance over four runs is reported (numbers within parentheses indicate the standard deviation). L stands for 'large' and wwm stands for 'whole-word-masking'. "+ Margin" refers to the second inference strategy explained in Section 3.4. Best scores are presented in bold, second bests are in italics (excluding the baselines).

senses following the standard in the literature. The statistics of the used datasets are provided in Table 1.

The classifiers are implemented using the Transformers library by Huggingface (Wolf et al., 2020). We use the uncased BERT large model for the explicit relation classifier (Section 3.3). The model is fine-tuned for ten epochs with a batch size of 16, learning rate of 5×10^{-6}. To optimize the loss function, we use Adam with fixed weight decay (Loshchilov and Hutter, 2018) and warm-up linearly for the first 1K steps. The model is evaluated with the step size of 500 and the one with the best development performance is used as the final model.

We mainly compare our results against the recent unsupervised studies we are aware of (Huang and Li, 2019; Ji et al., 2015). Additionally, we report the performance of a number baselines and upper bounds to put the results into a perspective:

- **Most Common Sense:** The performance when the most common sense of each evaluation level is predicted for every relation in the test set (Expansion for the first level; Contingency.cause for the second).
- **Most Common Connective:** The performance when the candidate with the most common explicit connective (*but*) is selected for

every relation in the test set.

- **Gold Connective:** The performance when the candidate with the gold implicit connective is selected. This baseline also shows the upper bound of the proposed pipeline (see Section 3.
- **Supervised baseline:** This is the results of the BERT classifier fine-tuned on the implicit discourse relations.

5 Results and Discussion

5.1 Evaluation on PDTB

The results are provided in Table 2. Overall, the 4-way classification F-score ranges between 33.86 (DistilBERT) to 41.10 (GPT2-large) where three models outperform the previous state-of-the-art (RoBERTa-large, GPT2-large, GPT2-XL). Moreover, the performance is robust across different sense levels as suggested by its relative performance to the baselines in the more challenging 11-way classification.

In addition to the increase in the overall performance, the most substantial gain is observed in Comparison relations where the unsupervised state-of-the-art is improved by almost 25% points to 49.52%, bringing it closer to the supervised baseline (58.35%). The relatively successful performance in Comparison relations hold for all language models, suggesting that language models are good at detecting the cues for these relations.

Marginalizing over all connectives leads constant improvements with all language models. Marginalization yields average gain of 2.12% when with BERT-variants and 2.04% with GPT2 models. This step alters only a small portion of predictions, on average 10.1% of the predictions change after marginalization. Relation-wise Contingency benefits from this step most with the average increase of 4.20%. In order to have a better insight, we closely inspect the label shifts in RoBERTa-large's predictions which reveals that the most frequent label shift is from Expansion to Contingency relations (41.1%). These changes mostly occur when there is a clear mismatch between the top connective and others following it in terms of their sense. To illustrate, Example 2 presents a relation, label of which was changed from *Expansion* to *Contingency* where the top five selected connectives were: "and","as","because","since","for". Of these connectives, only "and" dominantly conveys Expansion whereas others commonly convey Contingency. Marginalization acts as a corrective step in such cases and saves the model from depending on the top-rank connective by allowing it to consider the connective predictions with lower ranks.

(2) *Experts are predicting a big influx of new shows in 1990, when a service called "automatic number information" will become widely available.* [IMP=because] **This service identifies each caller's phone number, and it can be used to generate instant mailing lists.**

Finally, as for 11-way classification, the same pattern also holds where marginalization leads to the average of 1.07% and 2.27% improvement in F-score and accuracy, respectively.

Model	Conn	Sense
always 'and'	9.38	53.15
always 'but'	7.00	13.96
BERT-base-cased	14.43	38.43
BERT-base-uncased	14.85	43.40
BERT-large-cased-wwm	**19.61**	**48.09**
BERT-large-cased	15.69	43.31
BERT-large-uncased-wwm	16.67	45.98
BERT-large-uncased	16.39	46.85
DistilBERT-base-cased	13.45	35.18
RoBERTa-base	14.85	39.39
RoBERTa-large	17.23	46.08
GPT2	13.87	35.37
GPT2-large	14.43	39.58
GPT2-XL	14.85	39.48

Table 3: The agreement in percent of the language models for connective and sense prediction (see text for details). The first two rows show the results when only the respective connectives are predicted for all relations.

5.2 Evaluation of the Language Models via Selected Candidates

In order to investigate how well the language models perform their task, we present in Table 3 the agreement between the human-annotated implicit connective and each model's top-ranked connective[4] (column *Conn*) as well as the agreement between the most frequent sense of that top-ranked connective and the gold sense label (column *Sense*). From the low connective agreement figures, we see

[4]We limit this analysis only to the relations annotated with an one-word gold implicit connective due to our design criteria (see Section 3.1).

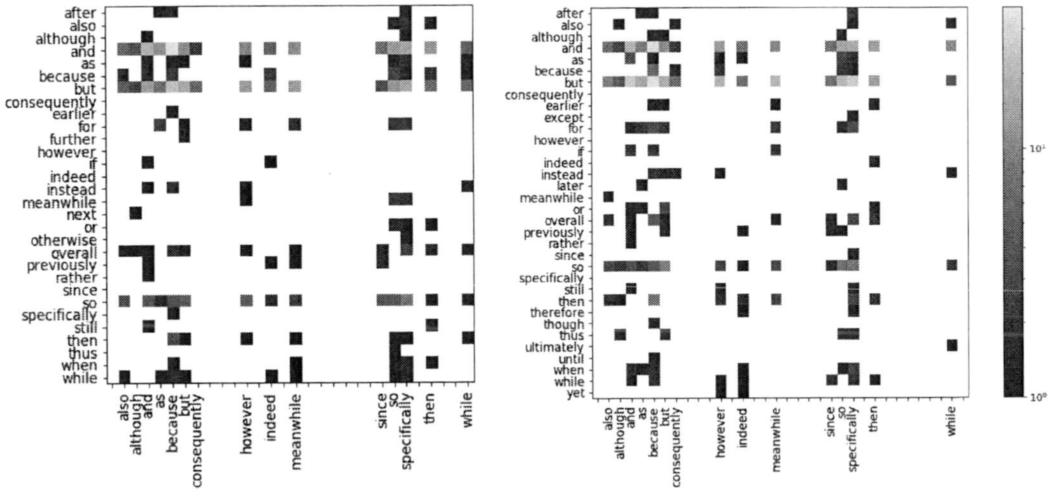

(a) RoBERTa-large

(b) GPT2-large

Figure 2: The (truncated) confusion matrices between the predicted and gold connectives of the implicit relations in PDTB 2.0 test set. The matrices are confined to relations with one of the most frequent 10 implicit connectives for readability purposes. The x-axis presents the gold connectives whereas the y-axis shows the predictions.

that the models generally fail to prioritize the connective favored by the annotators; yet, as evidenced by the high sense agreement, they are able to select a connective which suits the given context and thereby helps the explicit relation classifier. We further illustrate the connective predictions of the top language models from each family (RoBERTa-large and GPT2-large) via confusion matrices in Figure 2. As can be seen, the connective predictions are very scattered showing that language models struggle to predict annotators' decisions. However, we would like to note that matching human annotators' performance in connective insertion does not yield informative insights due to ambiguity; that is, for many implicit relations, there are multiple connectives that work as fine. Therefore, we suggest the evaluation focusing on the sense conveyed by the implicit relation and the connective (column *Sense*) as a more reliable way to assess the language models' performance.

too harsh a criteria to assess the language models since in many cases, there are more than one possible connectives that work as fine. Therefore, we would like to note that the second evaluation, matching the sense

Table 3 also suggests that BERT-based models perform better when it comes to selecting a suitable connective than the GPT2 family. We hypothesize that this is because bidirectional gap-filling language models have a training objective that is very close to the type of candidates we use. Finally, despite yielding the worst results, DistilBERT can retain most of BERT-base's performance ($\sim 97\%$), proving that even the smaller models can be utilized for the current task.

5.3 Cross-domain Evaluation

The limited number of the manual annotations does not account for the whole data bottleneck problem in discourse parsing, as the available corpora lack textual variety as much as numbers. Inarguably, PDTB is used as both the training and validation data in the bulk of studies; hence, most research on discourse parsing is confined to one domain. Unfortunately, initial attempts show that sub-tasks of discourse parsing generalize poorly across-domains (Stepanov and Riccardi, 2014).

In order to test how our pipeline generalizes to another domain, we run a set of experiments on the Biomedical Discourse Relation Bank (BioDRB) (Prasad et al., 2011). BioDRB closely follows the PDTB 2.0 annotation framework[5] and is annotated over 24 full-text articles in the biomedical domain which is quite different from that of PDTB. Probably due to this difference and its relatively smaller size, BioDRB is mostly overlooked in computational studies. Consequently, there are only few

[5] Yet, BioDRB uses slightly different sense hierarchy. We follow the instructions on (Prasad et al., 2011) to map the senses back to PDTB 2.0 hierarchy.

	Test set				Full Data			
	4-way		11-way		4-way		11-way	
	Acc	F1	Acc	F1	Acc	F1	Acc	F1
Bi-LSTM baseline	-	-	32.97	-	-	-	-	-
(Bai and Zhao, 2018)	-	-	29.52	-	-	-	-	-
MaxEnt baseline	58.44	26.64	-	-	-	-	-	-
(Shi and Demberg, 2019b)	77.34	43.03	45.19	-	-	-	-	-
BERT-base-uncased	54.15	30.29	36.98	14.59	54.90	36.30	33.80	13.99
+ Margin	52.11	30.15	36.69	15.41	55.15	37.46	35.75	14.59
BERT-large-cased	75.37	26.51	37.12	10.29	72.28	30.11	32.19	8.28
+ Margin	70.57	25.62	34.53	10.74	68.69	31.21	31.82	10.07
BERT-large-cased-wwm	62.36	24.59	32.95	10.87	65.36	33.59	31.81	11.39
+ Margin	56.99	24.79	31.37	11.18	59.83	33.10	31.20	11.90
BERT-large-uncased	58.05	30.43	35.25	12.82	57.32	36.21	34.23	13.85
+ Margin	57.24	31.84	37.99	15.58	57.01	37.73	35.23	14.54
BERT-large-uncased-wwm	61.22	32.24	**38.27**	15.29	60.05	37.49	34.58	14.09
+ Margin	51.95	30.39	36.83	15.62	53.98	37.03	34.40	14.55
DistilBERT-base-cased	39.51	23.62	21.44	11.77	41.21	28.93	21.78	10.47
+ Margin	40.00	27.78	25.32	14.97	38.35	30.43	23.89	11.56
GPT2	59.11	24.36	30.94	11.29	62.85	32.37	29.82	10.44
+ Margin	58.86	24.53	30.36	12.15	62.12	33.69	30.66	11.62
GPT2-large	62.85	29.70	36.69	**19.17**	62.47	36.59	33.08	12.97
+ Margin	60.81	29.48	34.82	15.18	61.91	38.33	33.86	13.61
GPT2-XL	58.86	**33.54**	35.11	16.23	59.19	39.86	34.22	14.75
+ Margin	56.75	33.17	34.53	12.54	59.19	**41.28**	**35.33**	**15.25**
RoBERTa-base	**78.70**	29.70	37.84	12.92	**74.73**	33.52	33.45	10.22
+ Margin	78.05	28.83	37.41	13.55	74.67	34.31	34.13	10.98
RoBERTa-large	71.38	28.44	37.84	13.21	71.26	35.77	32.42	11.25
+ Margin	70.98	28.46	38.13	13.49	71.42	37.71	33.70	12.93

Table 4: The results of the cross-domain experiments on BioDRB set. Test set refers to the results on the designated test set of BioDRB whereas Full data is the whole corpus. All baselines are supervised and their results are taken from (Shi and Demberg, 2019b).

results on BioDRB and unsurprisingly they are all from supervised methods. We compare our results with (Shi and Demberg, 2019b) which reports the state-of-the-art cross-domain results, along with the results from a number of baselines. For the sake of comparability, we follow their experimental settings and report both 4- and 11-way classification results on the BioDRB test set[6].

Additionally, as a more rigorous evaluation, we also report results on the whole BioDRB corpus. That way, we aim to free the evaluation of the generalization abilities of our pipeline from any bias that may rise from using a certain sub-part of the corpus. Finally, it must be noted that the LMs are not fine-tuned in any way on the target corpus (BioDRB) in either setting. The results are provided in Table 4.

The results suggest that our pipeline has strong cross-domain performance despite explicit relation classifier's being trained on only PDTB. In both 4-way and 11-way classification, we are able to outperform the zero-shot performance of even the supervised approaches, including the recent neural approaches (Bai and Zhao, 2018). We hypothesize that our two-step pipeline plays the key role in mitigating the domain-specific problems. Since we are using the "raw" (unfinetuned) language models to rank candidates, we are able to directly leverage the knowledge of these models that they learn from numerous domains thanks to their diverse training

[6] which is originally suggested by (Xu et al., 2012) and consists of the files *GENIA_1421503* and *GENIA_1513057*

data. Once the suitable connectives are highlighted by the language model, the explicit relation classifier can mainly rely on them to make the prediction; hence, less affected by the domain change.

6 Conclusions

In addition to its inherent difficulty, implicit discourse relation classification becomes even more challenging with the lack of sufficient data. In the current study, we focus on the latter problem by assuming the extreme low-resource scenario where there are no labeled implicit discourse relations. The data shortage is mitigated by leveraging the contextual information of the available pre-trained language models through explicitation of the implicit relations. We show that the proposed pipeline, despite its simplicity, is able to outperform the previous attempts. Furthermore, by taking another step, we tested the proposed architecture in the more challenging 11-way setting as well as on a completely different domain. The experimental results confirm that our model is robust and generalizes well, even compared to recent supervised approaches.

Acknowledgments

We would like to thank Dmitry Nikolaev, Johan Sjons, Bernhard Wälchli and Faruk Büyüktekin for their useful comments. The three outstanding reviews from the workshop also helped us greatly. We thank NVIDIA for their GPU grant, and the Swedish National Infrastructure For Computing (SNIC) for providing computational resources under Project 2020/33-26.

References

Hongxiao Bai and Hai Zhao. 2018. Deep enhanced representation for implicit discourse relation recognition. In *Proceedings of the 27th International Conference on Computational Linguistics*, pages 571–583, Santa Fe, New Mexico, USA. Association for Computational Linguistics.

Chloé Braud and Pascal Denis. 2014. Combining natural and artificial examples to improve implicit discourse relation identification. In *Proceedings of COLING 2014, the 25th International Conference on Computational Linguistics: Technical Papers*, pages 1694–1705, Dublin, Ireland. Dublin City University and Association for Computational Linguistics.

Jacob Devlin, Ming-Wei Chang, Kenton Lee, and Kristina Toutanova. 2019. Bert: Pre-training of deep bidirectional transformers for language understanding. In *NAACL-HLT (1)*.

Hsin-Ping Huang and Junyi Jessy Li. 2019. Unsupervised adversarial domain adaptation for implicit discourse relation classification. In *Proceedings of the 23rd Conference on Computational Natural Language Learning (CoNLL)*, pages 686–695, Hong Kong, China. Association for Computational Linguistics.

Yangfeng Ji, Gongbo Zhang, and Jacob Eisenstein. 2015. Closing the gap: Domain adaptation from explicit to implicit discourse relations. In *Proceedings of the 2015 Conference on Empirical Methods in Natural Language Processing*, pages 2219–2224.

Najoung Kim, Song Feng, Chulaka Gunasekara, and Luis Lastras. 2020. Implicit discourse relation classification: We need to talk about evaluation. In *Proceedings of the 58th Annual Meeting of the Association for Computational Linguistics*, pages 5404–5414, Online. Association for Computational Linguistics.

Man Lan, Jianxiang Wang, Yuanbin Wu, Zheng-Yu Niu, and Haifeng Wang. 2017. Multi-task attention-based neural networks for implicit discourse relationship representation and identification. In *Proceedings of the 2017 Conference on Empirical Methods in Natural Language Processing*, pages 1299–1308, Copenhagen, Denmark. Association for Computational Linguistics.

Yang Liu, Sujian Li, Xiaodong Zhang, and Zhifang Sui. 2016. Implicit discourse relation classification via multi-task neural networks. In *Proceedings of the Thirtieth AAAI Conference on Artificial Intelligence*, pages 2750–2756.

Yinhan Liu, Myle Ott, Naman Goyal, Jingfei Du, Mandar Joshi, Danqi Chen, Omer Levy, Mike Lewis, Luke Zettlemoyer, and Veselin Stoyanov. 2019. Roberta: A robustly optimized bert pretraining approach. *arXiv preprint arXiv:1907.11692*.

Ilya Loshchilov and Frank Hutter. 2018. Fixing weight decay regularization in adam. *arXiv preprint ArXiv:1711.05101*.

Daniel Marcu and Abdessamad Echihabi. 2002. An unsupervised approach to recognizing discourse relations. In *Proceedings of the 40th annual meeting of the association for computational linguistics*, pages 368–375.

Allen Nie, Erin Bennett, and Noah Goodman. 2019. DisSent: Learning sentence representations from explicit discourse relations. In *Proceedings of the 57th Annual Meeting of the Association for Computational Linguistics*, pages 4497–4510, Florence, Italy. Association for Computational Linguistics.

Emily Pitler, Annie Louis, and Ani Nenkova. 2009. Automatic sense prediction for implicit discourse relations in text. In *Proceedings of the Joint Conference of the 47th Annual Meeting of the ACL and the*

4th International Joint Conference on Natural Language Processing of the AFNLP*, pages 683–691.

Emily Pitler and Ani Nenkova. 2009. Using syntax to disambiguate explicit discourse connectives in text. In *Proceedings of the ACL-IJCNLP 2009 Conference Short Papers*, pages 13–16, Suntec, Singapore. Association for Computational Linguistics.

Rashmi Prasad, Nikhil Dinesh, Alan Lee, Eleni Miltsakaki, Livio Robaldo, Aravind K Joshi, and Bonnie L Webber. 2008. The penn discourse treebank 2.0. In *In Proceedings of the 6th International Conference on Language Resources and Evaluation (LREC)*.

Rashmi Prasad, Susan McRoy, Nadya Frid, Aravind Joshi, and Hong Yu. 2011. The biomedical discourse relation bank. *BMC bioinformatics*, 12(1):1–18.

Lianhui Qin, Zhisong Zhang, Hai Zhao, Zhiting Hu, and Eric Xing. 2017. Adversarial connective-exploiting networks for implicit discourse relation classification. In *Proceedings of the 55th Annual Meeting of the Association for Computational Linguistics (Volume 1: Long Papers)*, pages 1006–1017, Vancouver, Canada. Association for Computational Linguistics.

Alec Radford, Jeffrey Wu, Rewon Child, David Luan, Dario Amodei, and Ilya Sutskever. 2019. Language models are unsupervised multitask learners. *OpenAI blog*, 1(8):9.

Attapol Rutherford and Nianwen Xue. 2015. Improving the inference of implicit discourse relations via classifying explicit discourse connectives. In *Proceedings of the 2015 Conference of the North American Chapter of the Association for Computational Linguistics: Human Language Technologies*, pages 799–808, Denver, Colorado. Association for Computational Linguistics.

Victor Sanh, Lysandre Debut, Julien Chaumond, and Thomas Wolf. 2019. Distilbert, a distilled version of bert: smaller, faster, cheaper and lighter. *arXiv preprint arXiv:1910.01108*.

Wei Shi and Vera Demberg. 2019a. Learning to explicitate connectives with Seq2Seq network for implicit discourse relation classification. In *Proceedings of the 13th International Conference on Computational Semantics - Long Papers*, pages 188–199, Gothenburg, Sweden. Association for Computational Linguistics.

Wei Shi and Vera Demberg. 2019b. Next sentence prediction helps implicit discourse relation classification within and across domains. In *Proceedings of the 2019 Conference on Empirical Methods in Natural Language Processing and the 9th International Joint Conference on Natural Language Processing (EMNLP-IJCNLP)*, pages 5790–5796, Hong Kong, China. Association for Computational Linguistics.

Wei Shi, Frances Yung, Raphael Rubino, and Vera Demberg. 2017. Using explicit discourse connectives in translation for implicit discourse relation classification. In *Proceedings of the Eighth International Joint Conference on Natural Language Processing (Volume 1: Long Papers)*, pages 484–495.

Caroline Sporleder and Alex Lascarides. 2008. Using automatically labelled examples to classify rhetorical relations: An assessment. *Natural Language Engineering*, 14(3):369.

Evgeny Stepanov and Giuseppe Riccardi. 2014. Towards cross-domain pdtb-style discourse parsing. In *Proceedings of the 5th International Workshop on Health Text Mining and Information Analysis (Louhi)*, pages 30–37.

Thomas Wolf, Lysandre Debut, Victor Sanh, Julien Chaumond, Clement Delangue, Anthony Moi, Pierric Cistac, Tim Rault, Remi Louf, Morgan Funtowicz, Joe Davison, Sam Shleifer, Patrick von Platen, Clara Ma, Yacine Jernite, Julien Plu, Canwen Xu, Teven Le Scao, Sylvain Gugger, Mariama Drame, Quentin Lhoest, and Alexander Rush. 2020. Transformers: State-of-the-art natural language processing. In *Proceedings of the 2020 Conference on Empirical Methods in Natural Language Processing: System Demonstrations*, pages 38–45, Online. Association for Computational Linguistics.

Changxing Wu, Xiaodong Shi, Yidong Chen, Yanzhou Huang, and Jinsong Su. 2016. Bilingually-constrained synthetic data for implicit discourse relation recognition. In *Proceedings of the 2016 Conference on Empirical Methods in Natural Language Processing*, pages 2306–2312, Austin, Texas. Association for Computational Linguistics.

Yu Xu, Man Lan, Yue Lu, Zheng Yu Niu, and Chew Lim Tan. 2012. Connective prediction using machine learning for implicit discourse relation classification. In *The 2012 International Joint Conference on Neural Networks (IJCNN)*, pages 1–8. IEEE.

Deniz Zeyrek and Murathan Kurfalı. 2017. TDB 1.1: Extensions on Turkish discourse bank. In *Proceedings of the 11th Linguistic Annotation Workshop*, pages 76–81, Valencia, Spain. Association for Computational Linguistics.

Zhi-Min Zhou, Yu Xu, Zheng-Yu Niu, Man Lan, Jian Su, and Chew Lim Tan. 2010. Predicting discourse connectives for implicit discourse relation recognition. In *Proceedings of the 23rd International Conference on Computational Linguistics: Posters*, pages 1507–1514. Association for Computational Linguistics.

Šárka Zikánová, Jiří Mírovský, and Pavlína Synková. 2019. Explicit and implicit discourse relations in the prague discourse treebank. In *International Conference on Text, Speech, and Dialogue*, pages 236–248. Springer.

Implicit Phenomena in Short-Answer Scoring Data

Marie Bexte, Andrea Horbach and Torsten Zesch
Language Technology Lab, University of Duisburg-Essen, Duisburg, Germany
(firstname.lastname)@uni-due.de

Abstract

Short-answer scoring is the task of assessing the correctness of a short text given as response to a question that can come from a variety of educational scenarios. As only content, not form, is important, the exact wording including the explicitness of an answer should not matter. However, many state-of-the-art scoring models heavily rely on lexical information, be it word embeddings in a neural network or n-grams in an SVM. Thus, the exact wording of an answer might very well make a difference. We therefore quantify to what extent implicit language phenomena occur in short answer datasets and examine the influence they have on automatic scoring performance. We find that the level of implicitness depends on the individual question, and that some phenomena are very frequent. Resolving implicit wording to explicit formulations indeed tends to improve automatic scoring performance.

1 Introduction

Automatic short answer scoring is an application area of natural language processing where short free-form answers written by students in an educational context are automatically scored based on the correctness of their content. They occur for example in science education (Nielsen et al., 2008; Dzikovska et al., 2010), but also in foreign language learning to measure reading (Bailey and Meurers, 2008; Meurers et al., 2011) or listening comprehension (Horbach et al., 2014).

In such a scoring task, answers are graded based on their content alone - in comparison to essay scoring (Attali and Burstein, 2006) where also linguistic form is taken into consideration. Thus, judging whether an answer is correct or not may require the resolution of a number of implicit language phenomena as a form of normalization. Figure 1

Implicit:
3 is the perfect amount,
2 is not enough,
3 is too many.

Explicit:
3 *scoops* is the perfect amount *of fertilizer*,
because 2 *scoops* is not enough,
but 3 *scoops* is too many.

Figure 1: Two (made-up) answers to the same prompt demonstrating how one can say the same thing with different levels of explicitness.

shows two answers that express the same content, but with differing levels of explicitness. How the content is expressed on the surface does not matter for the score.

In fact, the two answers in the example should be treated in the same way regardless of their explicitness. The only relevant criterion should be whether they convey the right content and thus show that the learner understood the concepts. While humans often effortlessly resolve implicit phenomena, automatic resolution of many of these phenomena is not trivial. However, we argue that resolution of implicitness is a kind of normalization step that can help to improve automatic scoring performance.

Most work on automatic short-answer scoring does not actively resolve most implicit phenomena. However, the c-rater system performs pronoun resolution (Leacock and Chodorow, 2003), but they do not report the impact of that single component. Banjade et al. (2015) perform implicit resolution of coreferences between entities in learner answers and entities in the question and similarly target ellipses resolution, where part of the question is implied in the learner answer, both by aligning concepts from the learner answer to the question. They

Proceedings of the 1st Workshop on Understanding Implicit and Underspecified Language (UnImplicit 2021), pages 11–19
Bangkok, Thailand (online), August 5, 2021.

report a positive influence on overall scoring performance. Another notable exception is information structure, i.e. whether the answer repeats parts of the question as researched through focus annotations by Ziai and Meurers (2014). They report only a minor effect on automatic scoring performance.

In this paper, we analyse which implicit phenomena occur in short answer scoring datasets. We then analyze the impact of implicit language on automatic scoring performance.

2 Implicit Language in Learner Answers

There are a number of linguistic phenomena that pertain to the implicitness of language and are especially relevant for learner answers. In the following, we describe the ones we considered as candidates for our analysis.

Coreference Coreference describes the phenomenon that the same entity is referred to several times throughout a text, often using different referring expressions (see (Mitkov, 2014)). The most prototypical example of pronominal reference is shown in Example 1, where *they* at the beginning of the second sentence refers to the same entity as *pandas* in the first sentence.

- Pandas live in China. They eat bamboo.
- Pandas live in China. **Pandas** eat bamboo.

Example 1: Coreference

Bridging Anaphora The relationship between an anaphor and its antecedent may be indirect, constituting the special case of bridging anaphora (Clark, 1975). Take for example the statement shown in Example 2. While this can be understood from the context of the first sentence, it is left implicit that the second sentence refers to the fur *of the panda.*

- The panda is ill. The fur is dull.
- The panda is ill. The fur **of the panda** is dull.

Example 2: Bridging

Ellipsis An ellipsis is the omission of content that can be derived from context (see Example 3). There, the second sentence does not explicitly state that koalas are *highly specialized*, too, which can however be gathered from the first sentence.

- Pandas are highly specialized. Koalas are, too.
- Pandas are highly specialized. Koalas are **highly specialized**, too.

Example 3: Ellipsis

Numeric Terms In numeric expressions, the head word, i.e. usually the measurement unit, can often be left out. In cases with parallelism to a previous sentence this is a sub-type of an ellipsis, in others it is not (Elazar and Goldberg, 2019). Example 4 shows an instance of the latter case, where the implication is that this sentence talks about age, indicated by the use of *turn* in front of *30.* Instead of saying that pandas *turn 30 years* old, this is shortened to saying that they *turn 30.*

- Pandas turn 30 in the wild.
- Pandas turn 30 **years** in the wild.

Example 4: Numeric Terms

Information Structure Another specific subcase of ellipses that is particularly important in a question and answer scenario is information structure (Krifka and Musan, 2012), i.e. the distinction whether the answer repeats given information from the question. Given the question that is shown in Example 5, *bamboo* is the focus of the answer, that actually answers the question. Focus has been automatically annotated for short answer data, although focus-based feature made only a minor difference in scoring performance (Ziai and Meurers, 2018).

- *What do pandas eat?* Bamboo.
- *What do pandas eat?* **Pandas eat** bamboo.

Example 5: Information Structure

Presupposition A presupposition (see Example 6) is a precondition that has to be fulfilled for a sentence to be true or false (Strawson, 1950). The statement *pandas no longer eat bamboo* presupposes that pandas used to eat bamboo, which then makes it a valid statement to say that they no longer do.

- Pandas no longer eat bamboo.
- **Pandas used to eat bamboo.** Pandas no longer eat bamboo.

Example 6: Presupposition

Restrictive vs. Non-restrictive Remarks Any appositional adjective and any relative clause (Fabb, 1990) can either be restrictive, i.e. necessary for selecting the right entity out of a set of alternatives or non-restrictive. In the question

Explain how pandas in China are similar to koalas in Australia.

in China is non-restrictive (because it is not meant to differentiate between different kinds of pandas living in different parts of the world). We could think of such non-restrictive terms as the explicit version of an implicit sentence. Especially in a learner answer targeting that question the term *pandas* can be used, implicitly meaning *pandas in China*.

Implicit Discourse Relations The relation between sentences is often marked by discourse connectives. In some cases, there may be a discourse relation that is left implicit. With regard to the statement shown in Example 7, there is such a relation between the two sentences, which is an implicit *therefore*, as the reason for taking the panda to the veterinarian was its dull fur.

- The panda had dull fur. We took it to the vet.
- The panda had dull fur, **therefore** we took it to the vet.

Example 7: Implicit Discourse

3 Implicitness Annotations

Short answer-scoring datasets can include very different *prompts*, i.e. an (optional) reading text and some question the student has to answer, coming from domains such as sciences, biology, or English language arts. To cover a range of different *learner answers*, we select prompts from two short answer datasets and annotate occurrences of the implicit phenomena within the learner answers given in response to these prompts.

This procedure has three goals: First, we want to assess the frequency of these phenomena in learner data. Second, we want to evaluate the effect of implicitness on the final score an answer receives, i.e. we ask whether implicit answers are on average scored higher or lower than explicit ones by teachers. And finally, we want to know the effect of implicitness on automatic scoring performance. We investigate this third question by extracting explicit versions of the answers regarding the different phenomena from the implicit versions.

3.1 Datasets

For our annotations we needed publicly available short-answer data in English where answers are full sentences and not only single phrases like in the Powergrading dataset (Basu et al., 2013). Ideally, there should be a larger amount of answers for a single prompt so that prompt-specific models can be trained later in Section 4. (For an overview of publicly available shortanswer datasets, see Horbach and Zesch (2019).) We consider two short answer datasets in our analysis. The first one is the Student Response Analysis Corpus (SRA) of the 2013 SemEval task 7 (Dzikovska et al., 2013). It consists of data from two different sources. The *Beetle* subset has 3k student answers to 56 questions about electricity and electronics. The *SciEntsBank* subset contains 10k student answers to 197 questions about different science domains. All questions have a reference answer and (among others) 5-way labels judging the appropriateness of the student answers.

The second dataset we consider is that of the 2012 Automated Student Assessment Prize (ASAP).[1] It consists of about 2,200 student answers to each of ten science-related prompts. The answers to four of the prompts were rated on a four-point scale and the others received scores on a three-point scale.

3.2 Annotation process

Our annotation study focuses on four of the phenomena we presented in the introduction. These are coreference, bridging anaphora, ellipsis and numeric terms. We chose them as we expected them to be relatively frequent, based on a short manual inspection of the data, and because they can all be annotated following the same general schema, which we describe below. Thus, we expected that they would have a larger influence on automatic scoring performance. For each of them, we selected prompts from one of the datasets that

[1] https://www.kaggle.com/c/asap-sas

Phenomenon	Dataset	Prompt	# Answers
Coreference	ASAP	8	100
Bridging Anaphora	SRA	LF_26b2	40
Bridging Anaphora	SRA	ST_31b	40
Ellipsis	ASAP	2	100
Numeric Terms	SRA	LF_27a	40
Numeric Terms	SRA	VB_22c	40

Table 1: Prompts selected for annotation of the implicit phenomena.

seemed to contain instances of that phenomenon in larger quantities. For the ASAP data, we randomly sampled 100 of the answers to the selected prompt. As some of the SRA prompts only have 40 answers, we in these cases selected two suitable prompts to arrive at a combined amount of 80 candidate sentences. Table 1 shows the chosen prompts.

Coreference, numeric terms and bridging anaphora were all annotated following the same pattern. An occurrence of any of these phenomena is marked by annotating the span, which is then linked to the last explicit mentioning of what is necessary to resolve the phenomenon. Take for example a sentence *30 meters plus 20 is 50.* Here, both *20* and *50* would be annotated and linked back to *meters*. Ellipses were annotated in the same way, but following the convention that the token before the ellipsis was linked to what is necessary to resolve the ellipsis.

In some instances, there was no explicit mentioning of what is necessary to resolve implicit into explicit. Depending on whether this could be inferred from the context we then either directly annotated these spans with their resolved form or marked them as non-resolvable.

3.3 Annotation analysis

All answers were double-annotated by two of the authors of this paper to calculate two different measures of agreement. The first one is the **token-level agreement** on whether a token was annotated as covering the phenomenon. The other is the **antecedent agreement**, which is based on the subset of tokens where both annotators agreed that a token was part of a chain. Here, we only check those tokens that were not the first item in a coreference chain. For those, we checked whether they linked to the same antecedent.

Table 2 shows the agreement results. The κ token-level agreement ranges between .74 and .86 for all phenomena, except ellipsis where it is only .45. Ellipses seem to be hard to annotate. While both annotators found the same amount of instances, they substantially disagreed what exactly to label. One example for such a problematic instance was the sentence *Plastic A is the most stretchy* that could be either interpreted as a normal superlative or as leaving out the head (*the most stretchy plastic*).

Antecedent agreement is .90 and above for coreference, bridging and ellipsis, but lower for numeric terms with values between .51 and .7. With respect to prompt VB_22c, this arises from the fact that many answers reference numbers for which the context suggest that they represent some kind of unit of weight, but while one annotator did not find the context clues sufficient to resolve this, the other linked these numbers back to the span *mass of beans* mentioned in the prompt question. Example 8 shows the prompt and an example answer where this occurs. While both annotators agreed on the whole numbers being *scoops*, the decimal numbers created disagreement, with one annotator linking them to *mass of beans*, the other marking them as unresolvable. Without disagreement arising from this particular phenomenon, antecedent agreement increases to .81.

- **Question:**
  Describe what the graph tells you about the relationship between the number of scoops of fertilizer and the mass of beans harvested?
- **Answer:**
  It goes in a pattern like 0 is on 0.2 and like one is on 0.7 and goes from even to odd.

Example 8: Annotation of numeric terms

Table 3 shows how frequently the different phenomena occur within the prompts. As we did not curate the two sets of annotations, the reported phenomenon counts are based on the first annotator, who is the same for all of them. The most prevalent phenomenon is coreference, with 97 out of the 100 answers we annotated containing at least one instance of it. The two prompts we chose for the annotation of bridging anaphora differ in the frequency of answers with bridging, as 80% of the answers to one of the prompts contain instances of bridging, whereas just 18% of the other do. With respect to ellipsis and numeric terms we find that 40% of the answers contain ellipsis, and that 30% of the answers to VB_22c and 50% of the answers to LF_27a contain at least one unre-

Phenomenon	κ Token-level Agreement	% Antecedent Agreement
Coreference (ASAP_8)	.74	.91
Bridging Anaphora (LF_26b2)	.86	.91
Bridging Anaphora (ST_31b)	.80	1.00
Ellipsis (ASAP_2)	.45	.93
Numeric Terms (VB_22c)	.85	.51
Numeric Terms (LF_27a)	.76	.70

Table 2: Binary token-level and antecedent agreement for the annotation of the phenomena.

Phenomenon	% LA w/ phen.	ø # phen. per LA	Scores of LAs w/ phen.	Scores of LAs w/o phen.
Coreference	97	5.0		
Bridging Anaphora (LF_26b2)	80	0.9		
Bridging Anaphora (ST_31b)	18	0.2		
Ellipsis (ASAP_2)	40	0.9		
Numeric Terms (VB_22c)	30	1.2		
Numeric Terms (LF_27a)	50	1.0		

Table 3: Frequency with which the phenomena occur in the chosen prompts shown in Table 1. For the label distribution, individual labels from left to right are: 0, 1 and 2 points for Coreference, 0, 1, 2 and 3 points for Ellipsis and *contradictory*, *irrelevant*, *partially correct*, *correct* for the other phenomena.

solved numeric term. Apparently some phenomena are more frequent than others even when selecting datasets that seem most suitable for a certain phenomenon. While coreference by means of pronouns is a common phenomenon where sentences avoiding it completely would look marked, students in a school context might be less inclined to leave out, e.g., units of measurement in an exam situation.

In Table 3, we also report on the question of whether explicit or implicit answers are scored higher by humans and find mixed results.

As only three of the answers to ASAP prompt 8 did not contain coreferences, we cannot compare how the assigned labels may differ between answers with and without coreference.

In the case of bridging, the two prompts we chose also exhibit different patterns. Within the answers to prompt LF_26b2, the majority contains instances of bridging and those that do not tend to be labeled worse, most frequently as *irrelevant*. The other bridging prompt, ST_31b, contains fewer instances of bridging, and those answers that include bridging receive worse labels, most frequently *irrelevant*. Therefore, a typical answer to the LF_26b2 prompt seems to be one with bridging, with those that do not contain bridging receiving lower scores. A typical answer to the ST_31b prompt on the other hand is one without bridging, with those that do contain it getting lower scores.

For numeric terms, while answers to the VB_22 prompt that contain unresolved numeric terms generally receive good labels of either *partially correct* or *correct*, the other prompt we chose does not exhibit such a pattern. There, answers with unresolved numeric terms are equally likely labeled as *contradictory* or *correct*. We also see very similar label distributions for answers with and without ellipsis.

Overall we do not see a clear trend, which is reassuring, as teachers scoring such answers manually are probably not influenced by the presence or absence of implicit language (although of course a controlled annotation study would be needed to confirm this). In the next section, we will check whether automatic scoring models are equally unimpressed by the choice of wording in a learner answer.

4 Impact of Implicit Language on Automatic Scoring

As we have seen in our dataset analysis, there is a large variance whether learners use implicit or explicit language. However, as in content scoring, only the meaning and not the form of an answer is important, both variants should be scored by an automatic scoring model in completely the same way. Many state of the art models heavily rely on lexical information, be it word embeddings in a neural network or n-grams in an SVM. Thus, the exact wording of an answer might very well make a difference, especially if one variant is much more frequent than the other and therefore only rarely seen in the training data. To asses the extent of the influence of implicitness, we perform in this section automatic scoring experiments that control for the implicitness of our annotated phenomena in the data.

4.1 Experimental setup

For our experiments we use Weka's (Hall et al., 2009) SMO Support Vector classifier in standard configuration with the top 10,000 most frequent token uni- to trigram and the 1,000 most frequent POS uni- to trigram features, and train a separate classifier per prompt.[2] Due to the small amount of answers, we perform leave-one-out cross validation.

4.2 Controlling the amount of explicitness in the data

In order to assess the impact of implicitness, we compare two versions of the dataset, making use of our annotations. In the **baseline** condition, the training and test data is used as is. In the **explicit** condition, we use the antecedent annotations to resolve any implicit phenomena to their explicit version and then train and test on explicit answers.

Figure 2 shows examples for implicit and explicit versions of the four phenomena. For coreference, we resolve every pronoun to obtain the explicit version. For bridging and numeric terms, we add what is necessary to resolve them. In case of ellipsis, we add what was left out.

4.3 Experimental results

Table 4 shows the results of our experiments. Because the SemEval labels do not have a natural order, we report κ values for them, but QWK for the ASAP prompt. For the two ASAP prompts, we only had 100 annotated answers and hence a much smaller amount than the full set of answers that is typically used to train models on this dataset. This is reflected in a reduced performance compared to other experiments on the same dataset, but the focus of our experiments is rather to assess of the effect of making things implicitly contained in the answers explicit than to achieve the best possible performance for a prompt.

Overall, making the phenomena explicit within the answers seems to be beneficial for their automatic scoring. For coreferences and ellipsis, we see slight increases of .01 and .03 OWK, respectively. For the two bridging prompts, κ increases by .03 and .07. Regarding numeric terms, for the prompt VB_22c we see a decrease of κ of .03, but even the baseline does not do well here. The other prompt we annotated for numeric terms shows the highest increase of κ .17.

4.4 Error Analysis

One obvious question one might ask as a student being graded by such an automatic system is whether it is beneficial to use explicit or implicit wording to get a better grade. We therefore also compare the average number of points a model trained on the original data assigns to either an explicit or implicit answer. This can be seen as analogous to our analysis of whether human evaluators favor implicit or explicit answers, this time examining whether the automatic scoring model prefers one over the other.

Table 5 shows the results of this analysis. For coreference, results are mixed. While the overall average predicted score of the explicit testing data is slightly higher, there are also answers where the explicit version receives a lower score. For nine answers, the predicted score drops by an average of 1.1 points when they are made explicit, but for 14 answers the predicted score increases by an average of 1.75 points.

Within the ellipsis data, being more explicit is beneficial. There are four instances where the predicted score improves by one point, and none where

[2] We also ran experiments using a fastText classifier (Joulin et al., 2016), which was however unable to generalize from the small number of training examples.

Coreference	
Prompt:	During the story, the reader gets background information about Mr. Leonard. Explain the effect that background information has on Paul. Support your response with details from the story.
Original answer:	It motivated him , He knew what Mr. leonard meant and that gave him incintive to try harder.
Explicit Answer:	The background information motivated Paul , Paul knew what Mr. leonard meant and that gave Paul incintive to try harder.
Bridging Anaphora	
Prompt:	One function of the bess beetle's elytra (the hard, black wing set) is protection. What is another function of the elytra?
Original Answer:	To help make the strangulating sound .
Explicit Answer:	To help make the strangulating sound of the bess beetle .
Ellipsis	
Prompt:	Draw a conclusion based on the student's data.
Original Answer:	Based on student data, I noticed that the trial two (T2) plastics stretched longer then most plastics in trial one (T1).
Explicit Answer:	Based on student data, I noticed that the trial two (T2) plastics stretched longer then most plastics stretched in trial one (T1).
Numeric Terms	
Prompt:	Describe what the graph tells you about the relationship between the number of scoops of fertilizer and the mass of beans harvested?
Original Answer:	Well 3 is the perfect amount because 4 is too many 2 is not enough.
Explicit Answer:	Well 3 scoops is the perfect amount because 4 scoops is too many 2 scoops is not enough.

Figure 2: Exemplary original and explicit variants of answers.

it worsens.

While the instance count for the SemEval prompts is low, numeric terms and bridging seem to exhibit different trends. For the numeric prompts, the prediction only changes for three of the answers, with the predicted outcome always improving, twice from *contradictory* to *correct* and once from *partially correct* to *correct*. For bridging, the outcome changes for five of the answers, the predicted label once changing from *partially correct* to *correct*, but worsening in the remaining cases, three times from *correct* to *partially correct* and once from *partially correct* to *contradictory*.

Thus, our results suggest that it depends on the phenomenon whether making it explicit leads to a more favorable prediction of the model. While refraining from using an ellipsis or leaving out the head word of a numeric term seems beneficial, making bridging explicit does not lead to the model predicting a higher score.

5 Conclusions

We find that implicit language does occur frequently in short answer data and that the phenomena we focused our analysis on can reliably be annotated in learner answers, thus showing that such data is a promising source for implicit language in a relatively controlled setting. We will publish our set of annotated answers.

As we find that making the answers more explicit improves their automatic scoring, a next step would be to automatically resolve implicit language into explicit, to enable examining this effect on a larger scale. Subsequent analyses will also widen the experiments to include more different implicit phenomena and resolve more than one phenomenon in the same set of answers.

Acknowledgement. This work was supported by the DFG RTG 2535: *Knowledge- and Data-Based Personalization of Medicine at the Point of care.*

Setting	QWK		κ			
	Coreference	Ellipsis	Bridging		Numeric Terms	
	ASAP_8	ASAP_2	ST_31b	LF_26b2	LF_27a	VB_22c
Baseline	.20	.50	.69	.55	.42	.14
Explicit	.21	.53	.72	.62	.59	.11

Table 4: Automatic scoring results for the training and testing on the original data (baseline) compared to training and testing on answers that were made explicit.

Change in Prediction after Making Explicit	Number of Answers			
	Coreference	Ellipsis	Bridging	Numeric Terms
Better	14	4	1	3
Worse	9	0	4	0

Table 5: Analysis of how the predictions of a model trained on original prompt answers differ for the original answers and their explicit versions.

References

Yigal Attali and Jill Burstein. 2006. Automated essay scoring with e-rater® v. 2. *The Journal of Technology, Learning and Assessment*, 4(3).

Stacey Bailey and Detmar Meurers. 2008. Diagnosing meaning errors in short answers to reading comprehension questions. In *Proceedings of the third workshop on innovative use of NLP for building educational applications*, pages 107–115.

Rajendra Banjade, Vasile Rus, and Nobal Bikram Niraula. 2015. Using an implicit method for coreference resolution and ellipsis handling in automatic student answer assessment. In *The Twenty-Eighth International Flairs Conference*.

Sumit Basu, Chuck Jacobs, and Lucy Vanderwende. 2013. Powergrading: a clustering approach to amplify human effort for short answer grading. *Transactions of the Association for Computational Linguistics*, 1:391–402.

Herbert H Clark. 1975. Bridging. In *Theoretical issues in natural language processing*.

Myroslava O Dzikovska, Johanna D Moore, Natalie Steinhauser, Gwendolyn Campbell, Elaine Farrow, and Charles B Callaway. 2010. Beetle ii: a system for tutoring and computational linguistics experimentation. In *Proceedings of the ACL 2010 System Demonstrations*, pages 13–18.

Myroslava O Dzikovska, Rodney D Nielsen, Chris Brew, Claudia Leacock, Danilo Giampiccolo, Luisa Bentivogli, Peter Clark, Ido Dagan, and Hoa Trang Dang. 2013. Semeval-2013 task 7: The joint student response analysis and 8th recognizing textual embodiment challenge. In *Second Joint Conference on Lexical and Computational Semantics (* SEM): Seventh International Workshop on Semantic Evaluation (SemEval 2013)*, volume 2. Association for Computational Linguistics.

Yanai Elazar and Yoav Goldberg. 2019. Where's my head? definition, data set, and models for numeric fused-head identification and resolution. *Transactions of the Association for Computational Linguistics*, 7:519–535.

Nigel Fabb. 1990. The difference between english restrictive and nonrestrictive relative clauses. *Journal of linguistics*, 26(1):57–77.

Mark Hall, Eibe Frank, Geoffrey Holmes, Bernhard Pfahringer, Peter Reutemann, and Ian H Witten. 2009. The weka data mining software: an update. *ACM SIGKDD explorations newsletter*, 11(1):10–18.

Andrea Horbach, Alexis Palmer, and Magdalena Wolska. 2014. Finding a tradeoff between accuracy and rater's workload in grading clustered short answers. In *LREC*, pages 588–595. Citeseer.

Andrea Horbach and Torsten Zesch. 2019. The influence of variance in learner answers on automatic content scoring. In *Frontiers in Education*, volume 4, page 28. Frontiers.

Armand Joulin, Edouard Grave, Piotr Bojanowski, and Tomas Mikolov. 2016. Bag of tricks for efficient text classification. *arXiv preprint arXiv:1607.01759*.

Manfred Krifka and Renate Musan. 2012. Information structure: Overview and linguistic issues. *The expression of information structure*, pages 1–44.

Claudia Leacock and Martin Chodorow. 2003. C-rater: Automated scoring of short-answer questions. *Computers and the Humanities*, 37(4):389–405.

Detmar Meurers, Ramon Ziai, Niels Ott, and Janina Kopp. 2011. Evaluating answers to reading comprehension questions in context: Results for german and the role of information structure. In *Proceedings of the TextInfer 2011 Workshop on Textual Entailment*, pages 1–9.

Ruslan Mitkov. 2014. *Anaphora resolution*. Routledge.

Rodney D Nielsen, Wayne H Ward, James H Martin, and Martha Palmer. 2008. Annotating students' understanding of science concepts. In *LREC*. Citeseer.

Peter F Strawson. 1950. On referring. *Mind*, 59(235):320–344.

Ramon Ziai and Detmar Meurers. 2014. Focus annotation in reading comprehension data. In *LAW VIII*, page 159.

Ramon Ziai and Detmar Meurers. 2018. Automatic focus annotation: Bringing formal pragmatics alive in analyzing the information structure of authentic data. In *Proceedings of the 2018 Conference of the North American Chapter of the Association for Computational Linguistics: Human Language Technologies, Volume 1 (Long Papers)*, pages 117–128.

Evaluation Guidelines to Deal with Implicit Phenomena to Assess Factuality in Data-to-Text Generation

Roy Eisenstadt
Ben Gurion University
Computer Science Department
Be'er Sheva, Israel
royes@post.bgu.ac.il

Michael Elhadad
Ben Gurion University
Computer Science Department
Be'er Sheva, Israel
elhadad@cs.bgu.ac.il

Abstract

Data-to-text generation systems are trained on large datasets, such as WebNLG, RotoWire, E2E or DART. Beyond traditional token-overlap evaluation metrics (BLEU or METEOR), a key concern faced by recent generators is to control the factuality of the generated text with respect to the input data specification. We report on our experience when developing an automatic factuality evaluation system for data-to-text generation that we are testing on WebNLG and E2E data. We aim to prepare gold data annotated manually to identify cases where the text communicates more information than is warranted based on the input data (*extra*) or fails to communicate data that is part of the input (*missing*). While analyzing reference *(data, text)* samples, we encountered a range of systematic uncertainties that are related to cases on implicit phenomena in text, and the nature of non-linguistic knowledge we expect to be involved when assessing factuality. We derive from our experience a set of evaluation guidelines to reach high inter-annotator agreement on such cases. [1]

1 Introduction

We investigate how to deal with implicit phenomena in text when assessing whether generated text is faithful to an input data specification. Recent data-to-text generation systems are trained on large dataset, such as WebNLG (Gardent et al., 2017), E2E (Novikova et al., 2017), WikiBio (Lebret et al., 2016), or RotoWire (Wiseman et al., 2017). Data-to-text systems are usually evaluated by comparing the generated text with reference text with metrics such as BLEU (Papineni et al., 2002), METEOR (Banerjee and Lavie, 2005) or BertScore (Zhang et al., 2020).

Yet, recent work has shown that neural generation models risk to create text that is not faithful to the input data specification (Wang, 2019; Chen et al., 2019a), by either introducing content which is not warranted by the input or failing to express some of the content which is part of the input. In fact, studies indicate that the training datasets also suffer from problematic alignment between data and text (e.g., (Rebuffel et al., 2020) and (Dušek et al., 2019)), because large-scale data collection is complex.

In response, new evaluation metrics are being developed to assess the factuality of text with respect to the input data. Goodrich et al. (2019) attempts to measure factuality by extracting data from the generated text using OpenIE techniques and comparing it with the original data. Dušek and Kasner (2020) exploit a Roberta-based NLI system to check bidirectional entailment relation between generated text and input data. Rebuffel et al. (2021) operate without reference text and use a QA-based evaluation method to assess whether the text answers questions that are generated on the basis of the input data.

In this paper, we investigate what it means for text to be faithful to data by revisiting human guidelines, specifically related to implicit phenomena in text. While manually assessing the factuality of text generated by a generator we developed on the WebNLG and E2E datasets, we encountered systematic uncertainties in deciding whether text was missing or unwarranted given the data. We faced such uncertainties in more than half of the cases we analyzed. We provide here a list of such cases that we categorize according to the type of implicit phenomenon which triggers uncertainty.

Our main contribution is a set of guidelines for human annotation of data-to-text datasets in terms of semantic alignment: does the text convey all the data in the input, and does it introduce unwarranted

[1] The guidelines are publicly available together with our annotated data on https://github.com/royeis/FactualNLG.

Proceedings of the 1st Workshop on Understanding Implicit and Underspecified Language (UnImplicit 2021), pages 20–27
Bangkok, Thailand (online), August 5, 2021.

```
#T1 <S>Ampara_Hospital<P>state<O>Eastern_Province,_Sri_Lanka
#T2 <S>Ampara_District<P>state<O>Eastern_Province,_Sri_Lanka
#T3 <S>Ampara_Hospital<P>region<O>Ampara_District
#T4 <S>Eastern_Province,_Sri_Lanka<P>leaderName<O>Austin_Fernando
#T5 <S>Sri_Lanka<P>leaderName<O>Ranil_Wickremesinghe
```

#Text The leader of Sri Lanka is Ranil Wickremesinghe, but in the Eastern Province it is Austin Fernando. This is where the Ampara Hospital is located in Ampara District.

Figure 1: Pragmatic Inference in WebNLG: the `leaderName` relation between `Sri Lanka` and `Eastern Province` conflicts under complex assumptions - leading to the realization with *but*. Is this warranted by the input?

or contradictory content.

2 Content Conveyed Implicitly by Text vs. Data

We report on observations gathered during a larger effort: to study the factuality of generated text vs. a data input specification, we sample (data, text) pairs from existing datasets, and synthesize new noisy pairs where we either add a predicate to the data side, remove one, or alter an existing predicate (e.g., transform a triplet *region(Ampara_Hospital, Ampara_District)* into *region(Ampara_Hospital, Northern_Province)*). Given these pairs (both original and synthesized), we manually annotate the pairs as either: **reliable** (text faithfully matches the data), **missing** (text fails to cover part of the data), **extra** (text hallucinates content which is not part of the data) and **perturbation** (a combination of missing and extra, meaning some of the content conveyed by the text was altered with respect to the input data).

While annotating this data, we identified systematic cases of uncertainty: We categorize six cases where the relation between generated text and the input data is uncertain, either because the text conveys content in an implicit way or because the input data entails additional facts. We give examples taken from reference text in the WebNLG dataset. We then provide statistics on the prevalence of these cases of vague semantic relation.

2.1 Non-arbitrary Labels in the Data

In WebNLG and WikiBio, entities are represented with strings derived from WikiData, which are often complex. For example, the label `Fall_Creek_Township,_Madison_County_Indiana` refers to a specific township. The label is not transparent, in the sense that one can infer from the label itself a set of relations: `Fall_Creek` is a township, this township is located in the `Madison_County`, which is in turn located in the `Indiana` state.

The relations expressed by the label itself are implicit: the fact that Fall Creek is a Township is expressed by an underscore, but one cannot infer that Fall is a Creek. Similarly, location is expressed by commas in the label, but for different entity types, a different semantic relation would be expressed by the same mechanisms.

The annotation question that arises is whether semantic relations conveyed implicitly by non-arbitrary labels should be considered a part of the input to be conveyed. In other words, if a relation expressed in the label is not conveyed in the text, do we deem the text to be *missing*, and conversely, if the relation is expressed explicitly in the text, is it warranted by the input?

2.2 Bridging Anaphora

Bridging anaphora are effective at conveying a relation between parts of the text in a cohesive and succinct manner. In general, the resolution of bridging anaphora relies on non-linguistic knowledge. Consider the example (data, text) pair in Fig.1. The bridging reference in *the Eastern Province* (meant as a Province in Sri Lanka) is based on the non-arbitrary label of the Province. The fact that this Province is part of Sri Lanka is otherwise not stated in the input as an explicit relation.

If we consider that the label structure provides information in the input to be covered in the text, does the fact that a bridging anaphora is used cover this data? If conversely we consider that labels do not convey data to be covered, does the fact that the bridging anaphora requires the knowledge that the Province is located in the Country convey unwarranted extra information?

Similarly, in an example where the data states `location(Palace, London)`, `builtBy(Palace, Smith)`, `builtBy(OperaHouse, Smith)`, the text includes: *The Palace is located in London. The*

```
#T1 <S>Andrew_Rayel<P>associatedBand/associatedMusicalArtist<O>Armin_van_Buuren
#T2 <S>Andrew_Rayel<P>associatedBand/associatedMusicalArtist<O>Bobina
#T3 <S>Andrew_Rayel<P>associatedBand/associatedMusicalArtist<O>"Armin Van Buuren,
    Bobina, Mark Sixma"
#T4 <S>Andrew_Rayel<P>genre<O>Trance_music
#T5 <S>Trance_music<P>stylisticOrigin<O>Pop_music
```

#Text
Andrew Rayel has performed the genre of Trance music which has its stylistic origins in pop music.
He has been associated with the following musical artists: Bobina, Armin Van Buuren, Bobina, and Mark Sixma.

Figure 2: Collective properties in WebNLG

architect John Smith also built the Opera House. The relation between the palace and the architect is conveyed through a bridging reference, and is entailed by the usage of *also*. Do we annotate in such a case that the relation is covered by the text?

2.3 Conjunctions

In Fig.2, the same entity is associated through the same property to multiple values (`T1, T2, T3`). The name of the relation indicates that it is collective (i.e., when `r(s,o1) and r(s,o2)` we infer `r(s, (o1,o2))`), and hence, the realization can flatten the relation into a single conjunction. In this particular case, the input includes repetition (*Bobina* appears both in `T2` and in `T3`), and the relation refers both to objects of types `Band` and `Artist`. The realization entails all the values in the conjunction are `Artists` (and not `Bands`). The fact that *Bobina* and *Sixma* are independent `Artists` is not stated in the input.

In other cases, though, repeated attributes are not to be understood as collective, but as successive events. For example, when describing the professional positions people took over their career. A sentence stating *Mr. X is president, a businessman and the host of a TV show* would introduce an unwarranted entailment (that the positions are filled simultaneously). Should such an implied conclusion be considered extra content unwarranted by the input?

2.4 Pragmatic Inference

In contrast to the monotonic relation seen in Fig.2, the example in Fig.1 uses the relation `leaderName`. The reference text relies on multiple phenomena to realize the following sentence:

*The leader of Sri Lanka is Ranil Wickremesinghe, **but** in the Eastern Province it is Austin Fernando.*

The usage of the *but* connective relies on multiple assumptions: First, the fact that the Province is part of Sri Lanka as discussed above; Second, the fact that a Province in a country has a different leader than the country would be surprising (meaning, the province is separated, the leader of the province does not report to the leader of the country, there are not two leaders for one region).

A similar example appears in a reference text, where the facts `nationality(Anders, US)` and `birthPlace(Anders, Hong Kong)` are realized as: *William Anders, a US national (**although** born in British Hong Kong).* The fact implied by the usage of *although* is the common sense assumption that being born outside of the US entails not being a US national. One more instance of this category is related to presuppositions. If the input data includes `languageSpoken(Philippines, PhilippinesSpanish)`, can we infer that this is the only language spoken in the country? This determines whether the realization *The language spoken in the Philippines is Philippines Spanish* is faithful.

The annotation uncertainty is whether such semantic facts pragmatically inferred from the usage of connectives such as *but* or *although* or from presuppositions are warranted by the input.

2.5 Measurements: Units and Rounding

WebNLG covers domains such as description of astronomical entities and airports. In these domains, many facts are provided as measurements. Units are not encoded in a systematic manner in the data formalism. Generators tend to complete these units based on commonsense or world knowledge inferred from the domain (either as part of pre-trained language models or from the data-to-text training data).

For example, in Fig.3, the `mass` property has a unit explicitly specified in the input. In contrast, the reference text assumes the units for the `periapsis` and `orbitalPeriod` properties are kilometers. This turns out to be incorrect for `orbitalPeriod` (which should be measured in days or years).

```
#T1 <S>(19255)_1994_VK8<P>mass<O>5.6 (kilograms)
#T2 <S>(19255)_1994_VK8<P>periapsis<O>6155910000000.0
#T3 <S>(19255)_1994_VK8<P>epoch<O>2006-12-31
#T4 <S>(19255)_1994_VK8<P>orbitalPeriod<O>8788850000.0
#T5 <S>(19255)_1994_VK8<P>apoapsis<O>6603633000.0 (kilometres)
```

#Text
The epoch of 19255 1994 VK8, which has a mass of 5.6 kilograms is December 31st, 2006.
Its orbital period is 8,788,850,000 kilometres, with a periapsis of 6,155,910,000,000 kilometres and an apoapsis of 6,603,633,000 kilometres.

Figure 3: Usage of units in WebNLG: the inferred units for `epoch` is incorrect.

The annotation uncertainty is whether text that leaves the units unspecified when the data has it specified is considered missing. Conversely, is the specification of units warranted by data input that does not specify units?

An additional uncertainty related to measurements is whether rounding in the text is acceptable: in the same example, would the text be acceptable with an approximate realization such as *an apoapsis of over 6 billion kms.*

2.6 Implicit World Knowledge, Implied Data, Redundant Data

Chen et al. (2019b) noted that data to text systems benefit from the introduction of additional background knowledge at training time, beyond the data observed in the dataset. Reliance on implicit world knowledge has become prevalent with the usage of large pre-trained language models which encapsulate such knowledge, such as RoBerta or T5.

In many examples, the reference text refers to the type of an entity, even if the type is not part of the input. For example, in Fig.4, the fact that Turner is a musician is not stated in the input, yet it is mentioned explicitly in the reference text. This fact is entailed by the type of the properties in which the entity participates, but it can be left under-specified.

In other cases, the input data includes facts which can be considered redundant: either they can be inferred on the basis of other facts, or they are covered by the interpretation of non-arbitrary complex labels. Consider the example in Fig.5, the fact T1 is implied by T4 and the structure of the label `Spaceport_Launch_Pad_0` which indicates the Launch Pad is located in the Spaceport. The text does not cover explicitly the fact T1 (that the launch site of the rocket is the spaceport), but this is recoverable from the fact that the launch pad is mentioned in relation to the spaceport. Should this text be labeled as *missing* part of the input?

Finally, we observe many cases where content explicitly expressed in the text is induced from predicates in the input. For example, in many cases in WebNLG, a configuration such as: `(City_X is_in County_Y, City_X is_in State_Z)` and the text conveys the induced fact `(County_Y is_in State_Z)` in a realization such as *city in county, state*. In this realization, implicit world knowledge indicates a transitive inclusion (city in county in state) but this chain is not explicitly present in the input.

3 Discussion

The review of the examples above illustrates the complexity of determining whether text conveys data in a faithful manner. In the same way as text conveys implicit content, we observe that the small data snippets currently used as input to data to text systems do not have precise semantics: are the relations collective, transitive, symmetric, time is not specified, entities are referenced with non-arbitrary labels which are interpreted in vague manner. As a consequence, we suggest that we should consider the task of aligning text with data as a text to text alignment, which demands the annotator to exploit world knowledge and common sense. We follow in this the approach of Dušek and Kasner (2020) who cast the task of factuality checking as bidirectional textual entailment and Rebuffel et al. (2021) who view it as question-answering. Our contribution is to translate this approach into more precise guidelines for human evaluation, taking into account aspects of implicit communication in language.

We have prepared a set of guidelines answering the uncertainties listed above on the basis of this general approach. Based on these guidelines, we have manually annotated 200 samples from WebNLG with two annotators. We found a high rate of samples in the reference data which suffer from poor alignment, as was reported in previous work for a variety of datasets (e.g., (Dušek et al., 2019)). We also find low alignment between our manual annotation and the automatic assessment

```
#T1 <S>Aaron Turner<P>ASSOCIATED_MUSICAL_ARTIST<O>Old Man Gloom
#T2 <S>Aaron Turner<P>ASSOCIATED_BAND_ASSOCIATED_MUSICAL_ARTIST<O>Lotus Eaters (band)
#T3 <S>Aaron Turner<P>GENRE<O>Black metal
#T4 <S>Aaron Turner<P>ORIGIN<O>United States
#T5 <S>Aaron Turner<P>ACTIVE_YEARS_START_YEAR<O>1995
```

#Text
Aaron Turner came from the U.S.
He is a Black metal musician who started performing in 1995.
He plays in the Lotus Eaters band having previously performed with Old Man Gloom.

Figure 4: Expression of implicit knowledge in WebNLG: the fact that Turner is a musician is not explicitly stated in the input

```
#T1 <S>Antares_(rocket)<P>launchSite<O>Mid-Atlantic_Regional_Spaceport
#T2 <S>Antares_(rocket)<P>comparable<O>Delta_II
#T3 <S>Delta_II<P>countryOrigin<O>United_States
#T4 <S>Antares_(rocket)<P>launchSite<O>Mid-Atlantic_Regional_Spaceport_Launch_Pad_0
#T5 <S>Mid-Atlantic_Regional_Spaceport_Launch_Pad_0<P>associatedRocket<O>Minotaur_IV
```

#Text
The Antares rocket is comparable to the Delta II, which originates from the United States.
The launch site of the Antares was the Mid Atlantic Regional Spaceport Launch Pad 0, which is also associated with the rocket Minotaur IV.

Figure 5: Redundant data in WebNLG input: T1 is implied by T4 and the form of the Launch0 label

tool provided by (Rebuffel et al., 2021). This indicates the task of assessing the semantic faithfulness of generated text in data to text remains challenging, both manually and automatically.

References

Satanjeev Banerjee and Alon Lavie. 2005. METEOR: An automatic metric for MT evaluation with improved correlation with human judgments. In *Proceedings of the ACL Workshop on Intrinsic and Extrinsic Evaluation Measures for Machine Translation and/or Summarization*, pages 65–72, Ann Arbor, Michigan. Association for Computational Linguistics.

Shuang Chen, Jinpeng Wang, Xiaocheng Feng, Feng Jiang, Bing Qin, and Chin-Yew Lin. 2019a. Enhancing neural data-to-text generation models with external background knowledge. In *Proceedings of the 2019 Conference on Empirical Methods in Natural Language Processing and the 9th International Joint Conference on Natural Language Processing (EMNLP-IJCNLP)*, pages 3022–3032, Hong Kong, China. Association for Computational Linguistics.

Shuang Chen, Jinpeng Wang, Xiaocheng Feng, Feng Jiang, Bing Qin, and Chin-Yew Lin. 2019b. Enhancing Neural Data-To-Text Generation Models with External Background Knowledge. In *Proceedings of the 2019 Conference on Empirical Methods in Natural Language Processing and the 9th International Joint Conference on Natural Language Processing (EMNLP-IJCNLP)*, pages 3022–3032, Hong Kong, China. Association for Computational Linguistics.

Ondřej Dušek, David M. Howcroft, and Verena Rieser. 2019. Semantic noise matters for neural natural language generation. In *Proceedings of the 12th International Conference on Natural Language Generation*, pages 421–426, Tokyo, Japan. Association for Computational Linguistics.

Ondřej Dušek and Zdeněk Kasner. 2020. Evaluating semantic accuracy of data-to-text generation with natural language inference. In *Proceedings of the 13th International Conference on Natural Language Generation*, pages 131–137, Dublin, Ireland. Association for Computational Linguistics.

Claire Gardent, Anastasia Shimorina, Shashi Narayan, and Laura Perez-Beltrachini. 2017. The WebNLG challenge: Generating text from RDF data. In *Proceedings of the 10th International Conference on Natural Language Generation*, pages 124–133, Santiago de Compostela, Spain. Association for Computational Linguistics.

Ben Goodrich, Vinay Rao, Mohammad Saleh, and Peter J. Liu. 2019. Assessing the factual accuracy of generated text. *Proceedings of the 25th ACM SIGKDD International Conference on Knowledge Discovery & Data Mining*.

Rémi Lebret, David Grangier, and Michael Auli. 2016. Neural text generation from structured data with application to the biography domain. In *Proceedings of the 2016 Conference on Empirical Methods in Natural Language Processing*, pages 1203–1213, Austin, Texas. Association for Computational Linguistics.

Jekaterina Novikova, Ondřej Dušek, and Verena Rieser. 2017. The E2E dataset: New challenges for end-to-end generation. In *Proceedings of the 18th Annual SIGdial Meeting on Discourse and Dialogue*, pages 201–206, Saarbrücken, Germany. Association for Computational Linguistics.

Kishore Papineni, Salim Roukos, Todd Ward, and Wei-Jing Zhu. 2002. Bleu: a method for automatic evaluation of machine translation. In *Proceedings of the 40th Annual Meeting of the Association for Computational Linguistics*, pages 311–318, Philadelphia, Pennsylvania, USA. Association for Computational Linguistics.

Clément Rebuffel, Thomas Scialom, Laure Soulier, Benjamin Piwowarski, Sylvain Lamprier, Jacopo Staiano, Geoffrey Scoutheeten, and Patrick Gallinari. 2021. Data-QuestEval: A Referenceless Metric for Data to Text Semantic Evaluation. *CoRR*, abs/2104.07555.

Clement Rebuffel, Laure Soulier, Geoffrey Scoutheeten, and Patrick Gallinari. 2020. PARENTing via model-agnostic reinforcement learning to correct pathological behaviors in data-to-text generation. In *Proceedings of the 13th International Conference on Natural Language Generation*, pages 120–130, Dublin, Ireland. Association for Computational Linguistics.

Hongmin Wang. 2019. Revisiting challenges in data-to-text generation with fact grounding. In *Proceedings of the 12th International Conference on Natural Language Generation*, pages 311–322, Tokyo, Japan. Association for Computational Linguistics.

Sam Wiseman, Stuart Shieber, and Alexander Rush. 2017. Challenges in data-to-document generation. In *Proceedings of the 2017 Conference on Empirical Methods in Natural Language Processing*, pages 2253–2263, Copenhagen, Denmark. Association for Computational Linguistics.

Tianyi Zhang, Varsha Kishore, Felix Wu, Kilian Q. Weinberger, and Yoav Artzi. 2020. BERTScore: Evaluating Text Generation with BERT. In *International Conference on Learning Representations*.

A Data Description

We sampled 100 pairs (data, text) from the original WebNLG dataset, and expanded it with 100 additional pairs of synthetic perturbation of the data side (addition or retraction of a triplet, or transformation of an argument of an existing triplet).

We manually annotated each pair with the following labels (as shown in Fig.6):

1. Factuality: OK
2. Factuality: missing - in this case, we annotate which of the input triplets in the data is missing (`#Missing-pred`).
3. Factuality: extra - in this case, we annotate a span of text which is not warranted by the input data (`#Extra-content-in-text`).
4. Factuality: perturbation - in this case, we annotate both `#Missing-pred` and `#Extra-content-in-text`.

Finally, we manually identify which of the uncertainties which make the annotation difficult. Each case is labeled with one of the six categories identified in this paper:

1. **Complex Label**: a label conveying additional or redundant data with triplets in the data is present in the data.
2. **Bridging anaphora**: it is necessary to exploit world knowledge which may not be part of the input data to interpret a bridging anaphora.
3. **Aggregation**: data is aggregated in the text relying on the semantics of a relation in the data (collective, distributive).
4. **Pragmatic inference**: data in the input is implicated by the text through complex pragmatic inference (through presupposition, scalar implicature, marked by connectives).
5. **Units and rounding**: measurement is conveyed with unit that is inferred from the data (but not specified explicitly) or without unit; measurement is realized in an approximate manner.
6. **World Knowledge, Redundant Data, Implied Data**: input data is implied from content conveyed explicitly in the text, but it is not explicitly realized. Conversely, input data is logically redundant, and a redundant part of the data is not repeated in the text. Final case: content which can be inferred based on the type of the relations in the data is made explicit in the text (e.g., specify that a person is a Musician or an Architect even though this is not explicitly stated in the input data).

Each pair (data, text) can be annotated by multiple "uncertainties".

B Data Statistics

The prevalence of the uncertainty labels over the 200 manually annotated samples is shown in Table 1. We found similar frequency of the uncertainties over the original WebNLG sample and the synthetic noisy samples. We observe that these uncertainties are systematic: we found them on more than half of the pairs that we annotated.

```
#T1 <S>107_Camilla<P>discoverer<O>N._R._Pogson
#T2 <S>N._R._Pogson<P>deathPlace<O>Chennai
#T3 <S>107_Camilla<P>absoluteMagnitude<O>7.08
#T4 <S>N._R._Pogson<P>birthPlace<O>Nottingham
#T5 <S>N._R._Pogson<P>nationality<O>England
```

`#Text`
N. R. Pogson was born in Nottingham in the U.K. and died in Chennai.
He discovered 107 Camilla which has an absolute magnitude of 7.08.

`#Factuality` **perturbation**
`#Missing-pred` T5
`#Extra-content-in-text` *"Nottingham in the U.K."*

`#Uncertainty`
+ born in the UK implies nationality - 4 (Pragmatic inference)
+ absolute magnitude has no unit - 5 (Units and approximation)

Figure 6: Perturbed data in WebNLG: T5 is missing in the text which also conveys data not specified in the input

Label	Bridging	Aggregation	Pragmatic Inf.	Units	World Knowledge
52	12	35	63	12	81

Table 1: Number of occurrences of uncertainty labels over the 200 annotated samples

The distribution of the labels of factuality on the original WebNLG sample is shown in Table 2. We found that 20 of the 100 instances of the original WebNLG data were annotated with a non-reliable factuality label (missing, extra or perturbation). On the synthetic data, 95 of the 100 noisy label were annotated as non-reliable.

Factuality	#Occ.	Label	Bridging	Aggregation	Pragmatic Inf.	Units	World Knowledge
OK	80	23	3	20	22	2	29
Missing	11	6	0	1	5	0	12
Extra	4	0	0	0	2	0	2
Perturbation	5	1	0	1	1	0	3
Total	100	30	3	22	30	2	46

Table 2: Frequency of uncertainty labels per factuality on the original 100 WebNLG samples

UnImplicit Shared Task Report: Detecting Clarification Requirements in Instructional Text

Michael Roth **Talita Rani Anthonio**
University of Stuttgart
Institute for Natural Language Processing
{rothml,anthonta}@ims.uni-stuttgart.de

Abstract

This paper describes the data, task setup, and results of the shared task at the First Workshop on Understanding Implicit and Underspecified Language (UnImplicit). The task requires computational models to predict whether a sentence contains aspects of meaning that are contextually unspecified and thus require clarification. Two teams participated and the best scoring system achieved an accuracy of 68%.

1 Introduction

The goal of this shared task is to evaluate the ability of NLP systems to detect whether a sentence from an instructional text requires clarification. Such clarifications can be critical to ensure that instructions are clear enough to be followed and the desired goal can be reached. We set up this task as a binary classification task, in which systems have to predict whether a given sentence in context requires clarification. Our data is based on texts for which revision histories exist, making it possible to identify (a) sentences that received edits which made the sentence more precise, and (b) sentences that remained unchanged over multiple text revisions.

The task of predicting revision requirements in instructional texts was originally proposed by Bhat et al. (2020), who attempted to predict whether a given sentence will be edited according to an article's revision history. The shared task follows this setup, with two critical differences: First, we apply a set of rules to identify a subset of edits that provide clarifying information. This makes it possible to focus mainly on those edits that are related to implicit and underspecified language, excluding grammar corrections and other edit types. Since the need for such edits may depend on discourse context, a second difference is that we provide context for each sentence to be classified (see Table 1).

	Store Asparagus
✗	Keep the asparagus refrigerated for five to seven. [Cooked asparagus is best within a few days.]
✓	[Transfer the asparagus to a container.] Label the container with the date.

Table 1: Examples of a sentence that requires clarification according to the revision history (✗) and a sentence that remained unedited over many article-level revisions (✓). Annotators and systems were provided with additional context, here shortened in brackets.

2 Task and Data

In our task, sentences from instructional texts are provided in their original context and systems need to predict whether the sentence requires clarification. We define a clarification as a type of revision in which information is added or further specified.

Systems participating in the shared task are required to distinguish between sentences that require clarification and sentences that do not. For simplicity, we assume all sentences that remained unchanged over multiple article-level revisions (until the final available version) to not require clarification. Based on this assumption, we create a class-balanced data set for our task by selecting for each sentence that requires clarification exactly one sentence that does not require clarification.

In the following, we provide details on the collection procedure and an annotation-based verification thereof as well as statistics of the final data set.

2.1 Data Collection

We extract instances of clarifications from a resource of revision edits called wikiHowToImprove (Anthonio et al., 2020). Specifically, we used a state-of-the-art a constituency parser (Mrini et al., 2020) to preprocess all revisions from wikiHow-

Proceedings of the 1st Workshop on Understanding Implicit and Underspecified Language (UnImplicit 2021), pages 28–32
Bangkok, Thailand (online), August 5, 2021.

Edit type	Description	Example
Modifiers	Insertion of an adverbial/adjectival modifier	✗ Try watching one game to see if you like it. (→ Try watching one game alone to see if you like it.)
		✓ Learn about some teams. Article: **Enjoy Football**
Pronouns	Replacement of a pronoun with a noun phrase	✗ Do not be ashamed of it with your parents. (→ Do not be ashamed of your choice with your parents.)
		✓ Stay true to what you want. Article: **Explain Cross Dressing to Parents**
Complements	Insertion of an optional verb complement	✗ Press and hold to take a photo. (→ Press and hold the button to take a photo.)
		✓ Keep on pressing to extend the Snap to up to 30s. Article: **Set Up Snapchat Spectacles**
Quantifier/ Modals	Insertion of a quantifier or modal verb	✗ Dry the shoe off with the hand towel. (→ Dry each shoe off with the hand towel.)
		✓ Avoid using too much water. Article: **Make Your Sneakers Look New Again**
Verbs	Replacement of 'do' with another main verb	✗ The change in temperature does the rest. (→ The change in temperature takes care of the rest.)
		✓ You should do this as soon as you are finished. Article: **Cut a Glass Bottle**

Table 2: Revision types and example sentences that require clarification from our training set (✗). Additionally shown are clarified versions (→ ...) and sentences that remain unrevised until the final version of an article (✓).

ToImprove and applied a set of rule-based filters to identify specific types of edits (see Table 2).

Sentences that require clarification identified this way are likely to share specific syntactic properties. Accordingly, it might be easy for a computational model to distinguish them from sentences that do not require clarification. We counteract this potential issue by relying on syntactic similarity to pair each sentence that requires clarification with a sentence that does not. Following Bhat et al. (2020), we specifically select sentences that are part of the final version of an article (according to wikiHowToImprove) and that remained unchanged over the past 75% of revisions on the article level. For the syntactic similarity measure, we calculate the inverse of the relative edit distance in terms of part-of-speech tags between two sentences.

Data and data format. We divide the collected data into training, development and test sets, following the splits by article of wikiHowToImprove. For all parts of the data, we provide the article name and the full paragraph in addition to the sentence to be classified. For the sentences that require clarification in the training set, we additionally provide the type of revision and the revised sentence.

Out-of-domain data. We collect a small set of data from other sources, following the procedure outlined above, to create a possibility of testing how well models would generalize beyond the type of instructions provided in wikiHow articles. For this purpose, we create a corpus of board game manuals that consists of modern games for which multiple print-runs and editions of manuals exist.[1] We apply the same preprocessing and filtering criteria to this corpus as described above. In order to increase the size of this data, we allow edits that go beyond the exact match of a syntactic pattern (e.g. we include ✗ *The price...* → *This unit price...*, which contains a small change in addition to the added modifier).

[1]Board games in this set include *Android: Netrunner*, *Brass: Lancashire*, *Champions of Midgard*, *Descent: Journeys into the Dark (2nd Ed.)*, *Feast for Odin*, *Food Chain Magnate*, *Gloomhaven*, *Istanbul*, *Le Havre*, *Root*, *Teotihuacan: City of Gods*, *T.I.M.E. Stories*, *Unfair* and *War of the Ring (2nd Ed.)*.

	#Sentences	#Tokens	#Types
wikiHowToImprove			
- Training	39 186	552 567	25 297
- Development	3 264	45 622	6 719
- Test	3 414	48 261	6 934
Board game manuals			
- Test	44	885	381
Total	45 908	647 335	27 331

Table 3: Statistics on sentence and word counts.

2.2 Annotation and Statistics

Previous work has found that revisions do not always improve a sentence (Anthonio and Roth, 2020). Based on this insight, we decided to collect human judgements on all edited sentences that would be included as requiring revision in our development, test, and out-of-domain data. We used Amazon Mechanical Turk to collect 5 judgements per edit and only kept sentences that require clarification if a majority of annotators judged the revised version as being better than the original version.

Statistics. Our rule-based extraction approach yielded a total of 24,553 sentences that received clarification edits. We discarded 1,599 of these sentences as part of the annotation process. In these cases, annotators found the edits to be unhelpful or they had disagreements about the need for clarification. Finally, we paired the remaining 22,954 sentences with sentences that received no clarification. Statistics for the training, development, test and out-of-domain sentences as well as for the full data set are provided in Table 3.

3 Participants and Results

Two teams registered for the shared task and submitted predictions of their systems: Wiriyathammabhum (2021) and Ruby et al. (2021). **Wiriyathammabhum** approached the task as a text classification problem and experimented with different training regimes of transformer-based models (Vaswani et al., 2017). **Ruby et al.** combined a transformer-based model with additional features based on entity mentions, specifically addressing clarifications of pronoun references.

Results. We evaluated submitted predictions on the test and out-of-domain data in terms of accuracy, measured as the ratio of correct predictions over all data instances. We compare submitted

	wikiHowToImprove	Games	Overall
Wiriyathammabhum	**68.8**	59.1	**68.4**
Ruby et al. (updated)	66.4	59.1	66.3
Logistic Regression	62.4	**61.4**	62.3
Ruby et al. (official)	50.1	56.8	50.2
Random	50.0	50.0	50.0

Table 4: Accuracy (%) of baselines and participants.

	Wiriyathammabhum	**Ruby et al.**	LR
Modifiers	53.6	46.7	**53.7**
Pronouns	**92.7**	92.2	73.4
Complements	**81.7**	68.7	59.2
Quantifier/modals	54.2	**55.4**	53.0
Verbs	**95.1**	70.7	78.0

Table 5: Test accuracy (%) by edit type.

predictions against the expected performance of a random baseline and against a simple logistic regression classifier that makes use of uni-grams, bigrams and sentence length as features. The results, summarized in Table 4, show that the participating systems perform substantially better than both baselines on the test set.[2] Compared to this high performance (66.4–68.8%), results on the out-of-domain data are considerably low (59.1%) and they do not exceed the accuracy of the logistic regression classifier (61.4%). We next discuss potential reasons for this and highlight other observations.

4 Discussion

The results of the participating teams and the logistic regression baseline provide some insights regarding the task posed and the data sets provided.

Task. The results suggest that it is generally possible to predict whether a sentence requires clarification and models can pick up reliable patterns for most types of revision. In fact, the per-type results shown in Table 5 indicate that the best participating system is able to identify over 90% of cases that require one of the following two types of clarifications: replacements of pronouns and replacements of occurrences of 'do' as a main verb. These two types may seem like easy targets because pronouns and relevant word forms can be

[2]Note that due to a software bug during the evaluation phase, we allowed team **Ruby et al.** to submit an *updated* set of predictions after their *official* submission.

found simply by matching strings. However, the results of the logistic regression model show that a simple word-based classification is insufficient. Not all occurrences of pronouns and 'do' require clarification (cf. Table 2).

On the other end, we find that required insertions of modifiers, quantifiers and modal verbs are hard to predict. In fact, the systems only identify up to 56% of such cases, which is only slightly better than the performance of a random baseline (50%). One reason could be that commonsense knowledge plays an important role in such clarifications.

Data. It is worth noting that the distribution of different revision types is not balanced and the overall results are skewed accordingly. In almost half of the test sentences that require clarification, the edit involved the insertion of an adverbial or adjectival modifier (49%, 840 out of 1,707). Predicting the need for such edits is particularly difficult because they often add only subtle and context-specific information. Replacements of pronouns form the second most-frequent clarification type in our data (23%, 398/1707). Both participating systems were able to identify over 92% of sentences that require such a replacement. The remaining cases are distributed as follows: insertions of optional verb complements (15%, 262/1707), insertions of quantifiers and modal verbs (10%, 166/1707) and replacements of 'do' as a main verb (2%, 41/1707).

One potential reason for the differences in results between the test data and the out-of-domain data is that revision types are distributed differently as well. In fact, the edits of sentences that require clarification in the out-of-domain data almost always involve the insertion of an adverbial/adjectival modifier or an optional complement (82%, 18/22).

Insights from Participants. In addition to our observations, the system descriptions also report a number of interesting findings. For instance, **Ruby et al.** found that pronouns requiring replacement are often denoting a generic referent or a type of individual, rather than a specific entity. Based on this observation, they perform several experiments in which they first identify pronouns that should potentially be revised and then they combine representations of the identified pronouns with a sentence-level system to generate predictions.

A more technically motivated approach is taken by **Wiriyathammabhum**, who build on the observation that the distribution of sentence labels (requiring revision or not) is generally unbalanced and that revised versions of sentences that required clarification may be viewed as instances of sentences that do not require further clarification.

Both participants discuss interesting approaches to the shared task and show interim results on the training/development sets. For details, we refer the interested reader to the system description papers (Wiriyathammabhum, 2021; Ruby et al., 2021).

5 Conclusions

Two teams participated in our shared task on predicting the need for clarifications, with the top performing system achieving an accuracy of 68.4%. Perhaps unsurprisingly, the main takeaway from both systems is that transformer-based models pose a strong baseline for future work.

Linguistic insights. An analysis of the different types of needed clarifications showed that certain revision requirements are more difficult to predict than others. For example, we found edits that introduce potentially subtle and context-specific shades of meaning much more difficult to predict than cases where generic pronouns are resolved. Nonetheless, we find that the best system is able to predict the need for clarification across all types with an accuracy higher than expected by chance. We take this as a promising result and as motivation for future work on this task.

Open questions. A number of unanswered questions remain: for example, we have not investigated what is a realistic upper bound for the discussed task. We did find that annotators are generally able to identify which of two versions of a sentence is revised/better and they generally achieve high agreement. However, it still remains unclear under which conditions a revision is seen as mandatory. It also remains unclear to what extent the selected revision types actually reflect general clarification needs in a representative way.

In a preliminary study, we originally assumed that revisions of board game manuals could provide us with useful information about when clarifications are necessary. However, we found the application of syntactic rules for finding such revisions to be of limited use. Our annotation further showed that people also have difficulty distinguishing old game instructions from revised ones. It is quite likely that some texts are simply too specific for annotators (and computational models) as they require too much specialized knowledge.

Lessons learned. From our results, we draw the following conclusions for future tasks: a focus on instructions on everyday situations as described in wikiHow is generally desirable to enable a distinction between clarification needs due to implicit and underspecified language on the one hand and clarification needs due to lack of familiarity or specialized knowledge on the other hand. To better understand different needs for clarification, it will also be necessary to consider additional types of revisions in the future. Lastly, more context should be considered, both on the methods side as well as with regard to the data itself, in order to be able to better identify subtle clarification requirements.

We are already implementing some of these lessons in a follow-up task that will take place as part of SemEval-2022. In that task, the focus will be on sentences that require clarification and systems will need to predict which of multiple possible changes represent plausible clarifications.

Acknowledgments

The research presented in this paper was funded by the DFG Emmy Noether program (RO 4848/2-1).

References

Talita Anthonio, Irshad Bhat, and Michael Roth. 2020. wikiHowToImprove: A resource and analyses on edits in instructional texts. In *Proceedings of the 12th Language Resources and Evaluation Conference*, pages 5721–5729, Marseille, France. European Language Resources Association.

Talita Anthonio and Michael Roth. 2020. What can we learn from noun substitutions in revision histories? In *Proceedings of the 28th International Conference on Computational Linguistics*, pages 1359–1370, Barcelona, Spain (Online). International Committee on Computational Linguistics.

Irshad Bhat, Talita Anthonio, and Michael Roth. 2020. Towards modeling revision requirements in wikiHow instructions. In *Proceedings of the 2020 Conference on Empirical Methods in Natural Language Processing (EMNLP)*, pages 8407–8414, Online. Association for Computational Linguistics.

Khalil Mrini, Franck Dernoncourt, Quan Hung Tran, Trung Bui, Walter Chang, and Ndapa Nakashole. 2020. Rethinking self-attention: Towards interpretability in neural parsing. In *Findings of the Association for Computational Linguistics: EMNLP 2020*, pages 731–742, Online. Association for Computational Linguistics.

Ahmed Ruby, Christian Hardmeier, and Sara Stymne. 2021. A mention-based system for revision requirements detection. In *Proceedings of the First Workshop on Understanding Implicit and Underspecified Language*.

Ashish Vaswani, Noam Shazeer, Niki Parmar, Jakob Uszkoreit, Llion Jones, Aidan N Gomez, Łukasz Kaiser, and Illia Polosukhin. 2017. Attention is all you need. In *Proceedings of the 31st International Conference on Neural Information Processing Systems*, pages 6000–6010.

Peratham Wiriyathammabhum. 2021. TTCB System description to a shared task on implicit and underspecified language 2021. In *Proceedings of the First Workshop on Understanding Implicit and Underspecified Language*.

Improvements and Extensions on Metaphor Detection

Weicheng Ma[1], Ruibo Liu[2], Lili Wang[3], and Soroush Vosoughi[4]

Minds, Machines, and Society Group
Department of Computer Science, Dartmouth College
[1,2,3]{first.last.gr}@dartmouth.edu
[4]soroush.vosoughi@dartmouth.edu

Abstract

Metaphors are ubiquitous in human language. The metaphor detection task (MD) aims at detecting and interpreting metaphors from written language, which is crucial in natural language understanding (NLU) research. In this paper, we introduce a pre-trained Transformer-based model into MD. Our model outperforms the previous state-of-the-art models by large margins in our evaluations, with relative improvements on the F-1 score from 5.33% to 28.39%. Second, we extend MD to a classification task about the metaphoricity of an entire piece of text to make MD applicable in more general NLU scenes. Finally, we clean up the improper or outdated annotations in one of the MD benchmark datasets and re-benchmark it with our Transformer-based model. This approach could be applied to other existing MD datasets as well, since the metaphoricity annotations in these benchmark datasets may be outdated. Future research efforts are also necessary to build an up-to-date and well-annotated dataset consisting of longer and more complex texts.

1 Introduction

Today we are drowning in a sea of social media posts. Metaphors serve as strong modifiers to the intentions and meanings of written texts. In the header sentence, the metaphorical use of the word "drown" in the sentence well expresses the worries of the speaker towards the large number of messages in social media, compared to the narrative version of the sentence, e.g. "There are a lot of messages on social media". As defined by Lakoff and Johnson (1980), metaphors involve words used outside their familiar domains. For example, the word "sea" in the leading sentence literally means a large body of water, but it is used metaphorically as a modifier to the phrase "social media posts" to emphasize the abundance of messages in social media. Similarly, people can "drown" in water, but not in messages. As shown in this example, metaphors are expressed by the context but not the aspect words themselves, and there are no limits to the number of the metaphorical parts of speech.

Metaphor detection (MD) serves as a strong component in the natural language understanding (NLU) pipeline, since NLU models cannot correctly process the meaning of written text without understanding the metaphors in the content. MD serves to aid the NLU models by figuring out the metaphorical parts of speech in each sentence. However, this is a difficult task since metaphors are carried out by long spans of text, not by the appearance of single words or phrases. Existing algorithms and neural models are not able to encode long contexts without losing critical information related to metaphors. Moreover, the lack of labeled data and the difficulties in labeling metaphorical texts are obstacles to MD research as well. Due to these issues, the research on MD is still in an early stage and has not seen the improvements observed in other NLP tasks in recent years.

To reduce the annotation difficulties, researchers have been simplifying MD to a classification problem on the metaphoricity of one word or a word pair in each sentence. Existing MD benchmark datasets are almost all labeled in this manner. While the VUA dataset (Steen, 2010) extends MD into a sequential labeling problem, it still limits the metaphorical parts-of-speech to be one per sentence. This setting alleviates the pressure of early MD models which are based on handcrafted features (Strzalkowski et al., 2013; Hovy et al., 2013; Tsvetkov et al., 2013; Gedigian et al., 2006; Beigman Klebanov et al., 2016; Bracewell et al., 2014). Nonetheless, the limitation overly simplifies MD and makes existing MD

Proceedings of the 1st Workshop on Understanding Implicit and Underspecified Language (UnImplicit 2021), pages 33–42
Bangkok, Thailand (online), August 5, 2021.

Sentence	Her husband often **abuses** alcohol.
Explanation	To use excessively
Example	Abuse alcohol

Table 1: One example sentence from the MOH dataset that is wrongly labeled as metaphorical. The explanation of the word in bold and the example come from the Merriam-Webster dictionary.

models inapplicable in NLU pipelines. Since Rei et al. (2017) first introduced deep learning to MD, recent models based on deep neural networks are already approaching the performance ceilings for the simplified version of MD. Given the growing power of deep neural networks, it is time to redefine the task beyond the simplistic settings.

To verify our hypothesis, we fine-tune and evaluate a pre-trained BERT (Devlin et al., 2019) model on all the MD benchmark datasets. Our model outperforms the previous state-of-the-art models with large margins, as expected. The evaluation results almost all exceed 90% in F-1 scores, suggesting that the existing MD settings and datasets are too easy for deep Transformer networks to solve. We also extend MD to a classification task on the sentence level by removing the labels about the candidate metaphorical words. While the results slightly drop on two MD datasets (0.32% and 3.44% in F-1 scores), they are still high, especially on trivial sentences. We believe it is time to expand MD to include sentence-level metaphoricity labeling and to be evaluated on longer, more complex texts.

In the evaluations, we uncover flaws in the MD benchmark datasets by analyzing the prediction errors our model makes. One example of the annotation errors is displayed in Table 1. While the word "abuse" in this context literally means "to use excessively", it is annotated as metaphorical in the MOH dataset. The problematic annotations might result from recent updates to the dictionaries or changes in people's habits in using English. This situation makes it difficult to label the benchmark datasets on the sentence level with the existing word-level annotations. To validate our concerns about the quality of the annotations, we clean up one of the MD benchmark datasets and have the new annotations checked by two native English speakers. We also benchmark the re-annotated dataset with our model. The same strategy can and should be applied to other MD datasets to keep the annotations up to date. We provide more details regarding the data analysis and re-annotation process in Section 7.

The contributions of this paper are three-fold. First, we report new state-of-the-art performances on three MD benchmark datasets to display the power of pre-trained deep Transformer networks on MD. Second, we identify and clean up the annotation errors in one of the MD benchmark datasets through manual analysis and validation, which will be made publicly available. Third, we believe that the current settings of MD are overly simplistic for deep neural network models to solve, based on the evaluation performances of our model. Thus, we extend MD to a sentence-level classification task and provide benchmark results on the three MD datasets. Our future research efforts will involve the construction of an MD dataset with sentence-level annotations and longer and more complex texts.

2 The Metaphor Detection Task

Following Gao et al. (2018), we apply both the sequential labeling and word-level classification settings of MD in the experiments. Also, we generalize the classification setting of MD to the sentence level, disregarding the aspect labels. We describe the three settings of MD as follows. For clarity, we use $s = \{w_1, w_2, ..., w_k\}$ to denote a sentence with k words.

Sequential labeling: Given a sentence s, predict one label l_i for each word w_i indicating whether w_i is metaphorical in the context.

Word-level classification: Given a sentence s and an aspect word $w_i \in s$ (usually verbs, with exceptions), predict the metaphoricity label l_i associated with the aspect word.

Sentence-level classification: Given a sentence s, predict whether s is metaphorical.

The first two settings of MD have been extensively studied in previous research. Since metaphors are expressed by the linguistic expressions, attributing the metaphoricity of a sentence to an aspect word overly simplifies MD. but annotating an MD dataset with complex sentences under the sequential labeling setting is too difficult and costly. We provide the sentence-level classification formulation of MD for higher annotation quality while avoiding annotating an MD dataset on the token level.

Dataset	Sentence	Label
MOH	He **absorbed** the knowledge or beliefs of his tribe.	Metaphorical
TroFi	To expect banks to **absorb** a cost without a commensurate charge defies logic ./.	Non-Literal
LCC	Thank Lyndon Johnson, his Great Society, and the **War** on *Poverty*.	3

Table 2: One example record in each of the three MD benchmark datasets. The bold words are the aspect words. In the LCC dataset, the target word (in italic) of the aspect word is also provided. The label sets are {Literal, Metaphorical} in the MOH dataset, {Literal, Non-Literal} in TroFi and {0, 1, 2, 3} in LCC.

3 Datasets

We base our evaluations and discussions on three MD benchmark datasets, namely MOH (Mohammad et al., 2016), TroFi (Birke and Sarkar, 2006, 2007), and LCC (Mohler et al., 2016).

The MOH dataset contains sentences from WordNet (Miller, 1995, 1998) examples and the other two corpora are collected from news articles. The average number of words in the MOH dataset (7.40) is much lower than the TroFi (29.65) and LCC (28.66) datasets. This makes the MOH dataset the simplest among the three benchmark datasets. All three datasets provide one aspect word and a metaphoricity label for each sentence. The label is associated with the aspect word. The LCC dataset additionally provides the annotation about the target word of the aspect word in each sentence. Different from the other two datasets, the LCC dataset annotates the metaphoricity scores of the aspect words in the set {-1, 0, 1, 2, 3}. In the experiments, we get rid of the -1 labels in the LCC dataset since it denotes uncertain annotations. We display one sample sentence from each dataset in Table 2.

The MOH dataset is constructed with 1640 sentences, 410 out of which are annotated as metaphorical. The TroFi dataset is made of 1592 literal sentences and 2145 non-literal ones. In the LCC dataset, 493 sentences are labeled as completely literal (0) while 1242, 1251 and 1838 sentences are annotated with metaphoricity scores of 1, 2, and 3, respectively. We perform 10-fold cross-validation on all the three benchmark datasets under the word-level classification, sentence-level classification and sequential labeling settings in the experiments for fairness.

Though there exist other benchmark MD datasets as well, we choose to use the above three datasets intentionally. The VUA dataset provides annotations for the sequential labeling setting of MD. However, it is not publicly available now so we cannot obtain the data. The TSV dataset (Tsvetkov et al., 2014) is also widely used, but its training set contains only a list of adjective-noun pairs without the context. Despite the important role the aspect words play in MD, the lack of context makes it improper to train or fine-tune deep Transformer-based models on the TSV dataset. Clues for the sentence-level metaphoricity prediction cannot be learned in the training process either. Thus we do not take these two datasets into our evaluation.

4 Related Work

Since MD is originally defined as a classification task, most early researchers solve it with logistic regression or SVM (Support Vector Machine) classifiers. To use the information in the context, researchers concern much about the interrelations between the aspect words and the words closely related to them. Thus POS (Part of Speech) tags and dependency paths are frequently used in MD research. Shutova and Sun (2013) and Shutova et al. (2010) group the grammatical relations between each pair of aspect word and its target word into clusters, and they use rules to find out metaphorical combinations. Topical information is also a crucial clue to the domain information of a sentence so it is widely used in MD. Jang et al. (2016) represent the domain distribution of a sentence with sentence LDA. They then base their metaphoricity predictions on the similarities, differences and transition patterns between adjacent sentence pairs.

It is interesting, though, that some words are regularly used metaphorically. The intrinsic characteristics of these words are often taken into account when solving MD. Strzalkowski et al. (2013) assume that highly imaginable words are promising metaphorical words. They lookup the imaginability scores of the aspect words in the MRCPD lexicon (Coltheart, 1981; Wilson,

1988) and label the words with high imaginability scores as metaphorical. Similarly, Bracewell et al. (2014) also consider imaginability in predicting the metaphoricity of words. Tsvetkov et al. (2013) and Turney et al. (2011) instead use abstractness of the aspect words or the entire sentences as features in detecting metaphors. Other word-based features include the WordNet features (e.g. synonyms and semantic categories) (Strzalkowski et al., 2013; Tsvetkov et al., 2013), the VerbNet features (e.g. thematic roles) (Beigman Klebanov et al., 2016), the domains of the candidate-words' arguments (Gedigian et al., 2006), and the named entity information (Tsvetkov et al., 2013). Jang et al. (2016) claim that metaphors reveal the emotional or cognitive features of the author, so they use the occurrence of words in the LIWC lexicon (Tausczik and Pennebaker, 2010) to model the sentences in their research.

Some researchers do not agree with the word-level classification setting of MD. Instead, Hovy et al. (2013) claim that every word in a sentence can be metaphorical or literal, making it unrealistic to list all the possible aspect words. They introduce the sequential labeling setting of MD and apply CRF (Conditional Random Field) to solve it. Researchers are actively studying MD as a sequential labeling task, but a well-annotated dataset under this setting is difficult to obtain at least for now.

Not until the year of 2016 did natural language processing (NLP) researchers start to use neural networks in MD. With the power of neural networks, more and more researchers begin to examine the use of longer-term context information in MD. Do Do Dinh and Gurevych (2016) encode the aspect words with an MLP (Multilayer Perceptron) taking the vectorized word embeddings, POS features and positional features as inputs. They predict the metaphoricity of each aspect word by feeding their encodings into a logistic regression classifier. Bulat et al. (2017) similarly use pre-trained word embeddings to represent the aspect words, and they use SVD (Singular Value Decomposition) to gain sentence representation for classification. Shutova et al. (2016) assume that the metaphoricity of a two-word phrase can be modeled with the cosine similarity between the aspect word embedding and the phrase embedding. To represent the aspect word and phrase, they slide a window of fixed size on the context and use the information of all the words appearing in the window to encode the central word or the entire phrase. They also introduce visual embeddings of words into MD which, according to their experimental results, help improve the results of MD on two benchmark datasets. Rei et al. (2017) extend the idea of Shutova et al. (2016) by calculating a gated cosine similarity score between the two words' embeddings in each phrase with neural networks. The research by Gao et al. (2018) consider the entire sentence as useful context information and use BiLSTM with the attention mechanism to extract the features from the sentence automatically. Most recently, Dankers et al. (2019) combine BERT with BiLSTM to jointly solve MD and the Emotion Regression task. Their model yields good results on MD, but it does not fully exploit the encoding ability of BERT. To go one step further, we design a BERT-based model and evaluate it on three standard evaluation datasets on MD in this paper.

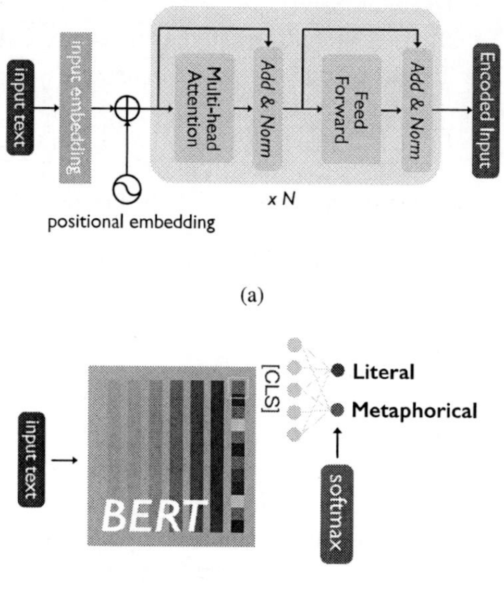

(a)

(b)

Figure 1: The architecture of Transformer networks (a) and our model (b). N denotes the number of self-attention layers in a Transformer model.

5 Model Architecture

The Transformer networks have been overtaking the state-of-the-arts in the NLP field since their emergence. However, there have been very few works that have studied the usage of the Transformer networks in MD. To the best of our knowl-

Model	MOH			TroFi			LCC		
	WCLS	SCLS	SL	WCLS	SCLS	SL	WCLS	SCLS	SL
Dankers et al. (2019)	-	-	-	-	-	-	76.90	-	-
Gao et al. (2018)	79.10	-	75.60	72.00	-	71.10	-	-	-
Shutova et al. (2016)	75.00	-	-	-	-	-	-	-	-
Rei et al. (2017)	74.20	-	-	-	-	-	-	-	-
BERT	**85.52**	**86.32**	**89.18**	**92.44**	**92.12**	**94.45**	**81.00**	**77.56**	**91.48**

Table 3: Experimental results on the MOH, TroFi and LCC datasets with the word-level classification (WCLS), sentence-level classification (SCLS) and sequential labeling (SL) settings. All results are in terms of F-1 scores. BERT refers to our model.

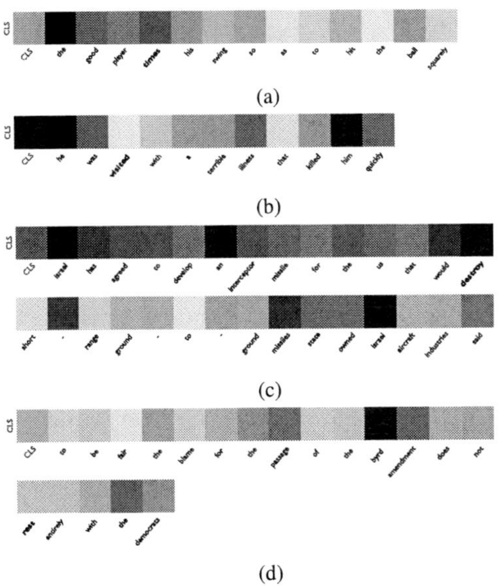

Figure 2: Attention heatmaps generated by our sentence-level classification model on the MOH and TroFi datasets. The words in bold are the aspect words.

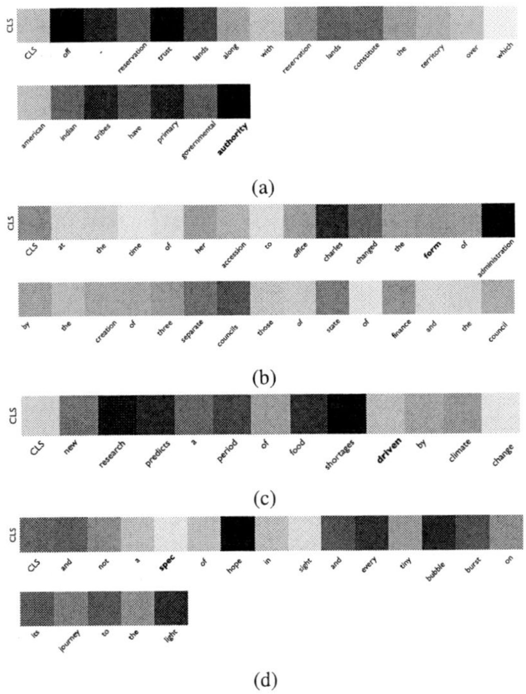

Figure 3: Attention heatmaps generated by our sentence-level classification model on the LCC dataset.

edge, Dankers et al. (2019) made the first and only attempt in applying BERT (Devlin et al., 2019), one of the most prevalent pre-trained Transformer-based models, on MD. They build an MLP or additional attention layers on top of BERT to make metaphoricity predictions. In our point of view, however, combining BERT with complex neural network architectures is a waste of its strength. The additional layers co-trained with BERT are only exposed to the task-specific dataset which is much smaller than the BERT training data. This makes it difficult to adapt BERT to the classification layers. It is good enough to simply use a linear layer to resize the BERT output to the prediction space. We specify the neural network architecture underlying BERT in Figure 1a and show in Figure 1b the simple model architecture with which we are able to achieve the state of the art on three MD benchmark datasets. Our experiments are based on the PyTorch implementation of the Transformer networks by Huggingface (Wolf et al., 2019).

6 Experiments

As is mentioned in previous sections, we fine-tune and evaluate BERT models for classification and for sequential labeling on the Trofi, MOH and LCC datasets with 10-fold cross validation. In the experiments, we use the pre-trained **bert-base-cased** model released by Google. The model architecture is a 12-layer Transformer model with 12

Dataset	ID	Sentence	Label	Pred
MOH	1	The house **looks** north.	metaphorical	literal
	2	The huge waves **swallowed** the small boat and it sank shortly thereafter.	metaphorical	literal
	3	You must **adhere** to the rules.	metaphorical	literal
	4	They **adhere** to their plan.	literal	literal
TroFi	5	At 9 p.m . , a doctor **examines** her and orders tests ./.	non-literal	literal
	6	The study , which **examined** 50 people who were wearing lap belts during auto accidents , concluded that 32 would have “ fared substantially better if they had been wearing a lap-shoulder belt . ”/”	non-literal	literal
	7	In order to focus federal resources on the SSC , its backers decided that Isabelle had to **die** ./.	non-literal	literal
LCC	8	From this calculation it is obvious that with any **form** of taxation per head the State is baling out the last coppers of the poor taxpayers in order to settle accounts with wealthy foreigners, from whom it has borrowed money instead of collecting these coppers for its own needs without the additional interest.	2	3
	9	The organism that causes gonorrhea (gonococcus) is an **example** of a bacterial invader.	2	3
	10	Background Checks - Local Background Checks Can **Reduce** Deaths.	1	0

Table 4: Example prediction errors on the MOH, TroFi and LCC datasets. The source words are in bold.

attention heads on each layer. The hidden dimension of the model is 768. We limit the sentence lengths to 128 since it fits most of the sentences in the three datasets. In both the fine-tuning and evaluation process, we set the batch size to 128. As for training epochs, we use 5 for the aspect-based classification setting, 20 for the sentence-based setting and 20 for the sequential labeling formulation. We select the training epochs through manually monitoring the training process to avoid overfitting.

Our evaluation is performed under the three MD settings respectively. For the word-based classification setting, we mask out the aspect word in each sentence and concatenate the pair of sentences with and without the mask as input. In this way, we take advantage of BERT's next sentence prediction mechanism. Since BERT infers the masked words with contextual information, it is highly probable that the masked word is used literally if the two sentences are predicted to be in the same context. In the sentence-level formulation, we directly feed into the model the original sentence without any change. The sequential labeling model takes the words and their indexes in the sentence as input and predicts the metaphoricity label of each word. We label the aspect words with their annotated labels and regard all the other words as literally used in the evaluation.

Table 3 displays the 10-fold cross-validation results of our model and the baseline models on the three benchmark datasets. Our model outperforms the baseline models by large margins and constructs the new state of the art under all the three settings. The success of the models based on Elmo (Peters et al., 2018) and BERT demonstrates the importance of contextual information in MD. By comparing our model to that of Gao et al. (2018) which relies on Elmo embeddings, we demonstrate the outstanding encoding ability of BERT. Though both based on the BERT model, our model shows superior performance in MD than that of Dankers et al. (2019). This supports our assumption that overly complex classifiers built on top of BERT negatively affect the fine-tuning process.

The results show that in most cases, our model performs the best in the word-based classification setting. The more complex the sentences in the datasets are (LCC > TroFi > MOH), the more difficult the sentence-based classification setting of MD is than the word-based classification setting. This agrees with our expectation since there can be multiple metaphorical words in a sentence that influence the prediction of our model. Our model performs surprisingly well on the TroFi dataset, even better than on the MOH dataset. This might be due to the difficulty of training deep neural models on the overly simple sentences in the MOH dataset. Our model shows great potential under the sequential labeling setting as well. On all the three datasets, our model achieves F-1 scores close to or even above 90%. We are highly impressed by the power of the BERT model and we feel that the existing MD benchmark datasets are becoming too easy for deep Transformer-based models to solve. So it is time to construct new corpora containing longer and more complex text with multiple metaphorical components in each piece of text. By extending the MD research to more complex realistic scenes, the MD models can better aid the NLU research and benefit the NLP community.

7 Analysis and Discussions

We manually inspect the predictions our model makes to analyze the causes of the prediction errors. Table 4 displays typical prediction errors in our evaluation. The major problem with the MOH dataset is the unbalanced labels for each aspect word. Grouping by the aspect words, 194 out of the 438 word groups in the MOH dataset contain no metaphorical annotations and 11 groups have no literal annotations. The labels in the rest of the word groups are not balanced either. Models trained on unbalanced training data are likely to associate the label predictions with the appearance of the aspect words. Sentence 1 in Table 4 is the only metaphorical record with the aspect word "look" in the MOH dataset, for example. The model might have learned to classify all the sentences with the verb "look" into the literal class, generating this error case. On the other hand, most sentences in the MOH dataset are simple and the aspect words are often the only verbs. This increases the difficulty of our model to generalize the learned knowledge into predictions on longer and more complex sentences in the validation dataset. Sentence 2 features the metaphorical word "swallow" but our model is disturbed by the literal word "sink" and makes the wrong prediction. As all the sentences with "swallow" in the MOH dataset are annotated as metaphorical, this prediction error proves that our model learns to classify not from the single aspect words, but a global view of the sentences. Some annotations in the MOH dataset are difficult for us to understand. For instance, "adhere to the rules" in Sentence 3 is labeled as metaphorical while "adhere to the plan" in Sentence 4 is literal. This leads to our hypothesis that the annotations may be wrong or outdated. With this idea in mind, we re-annotated the MOH dataset. In the resulted dataset, 402 out of the 1639 annotations (24.53%) are different from the original labels. To alleviate the problem caused by the subjectivity in the metaphoricity annotations, we sampled 100 from the records where our annotations do not agree with the original ones and had it validated with three native speakers. The agreement rate of the three independent annotators on the new annotations is 66%. This proves that our annotations are better in quality than the original labels. We use majority vote to re-label the MOH dataset and benchmark the revised dataset with our BERT-based model. The 10-fold cross-validation results are 94.21%, 94.21%, and 98.22% under the word-level classification, sentence-level classification and sequential labeling settings, respectively.

Our model performs much better on the TroFi dataset than on the MOH dataset, benefited from the abundant instances in each word group and the relatively balanced labels. However, we do not fully agree with the annotations either. The label for the word "examine" in Sentence 5, for example, is metaphorical, though the usage of "examine" in this sentence well aligns with its literal meaning "test or examine for the presence of disease or infection". Similarly, the "examine" in Sentence 6 is used in its literal meaning "to question or examine thoroughly and closely", but it is labeled as metaphorical. Since the TroFi dataset is collected from news articles, abbreviations sometimes cause trouble in the evaluation as well. The name "Isabelle" in Sentence 7 can well denote a person without preliminary knowledge about SSC (Superconducting Supercollider) in the context. It is then understandable why our model predicts the sentence as using the verb "die" literally. In the future, we suggest adding the surrounding sentences in the context into the dataset to make MD better defined and more appropriate for training deep neural network models.

Different from the MOH and TroFi datasets, the LCC dataset does not limit the source words to verbs. Another difference is that the labels in the LCC dataset are metaphoricity scores. This makes the LCC dataset more difficult to solve. Our model predicts 3 while the label is 2 for the word "form" in Sentence 8, for example. Possibly our model detects the metaphorical use of "copper" in the same sentence and decides to assign a higher metaphoricity score to the entire sentence. The prediction error of our model in Sentence 9 is in a similar case. Our model predicts a high score due to the synergy of the metaphorical words "example" and "invader". The annotations in the LCC dataset are sometimes controversial as well. The word "reduce" in Sentence 10 perfectly matches the literal meaning "to cut down on", but is annotated as 1 (weakly metaphorical) in LCC, for example.

On the other hand, since higher attention weights are put on the evidence for classification in Transformer-based models, we examine the attention maps on the last self-attention layer generated by our model under the sentence-level classification setting to interpret the performance of our model. Under the sentence-level classification setting, the predictions are made from the hidden states of the CLS token. So we evaluate the attention scores of the CLS token on all the other words in each sentence. The rule well applies to the word-level classification and sequential labeling settings, only with different tokens on which to base the predictions. To avoid duplication, we only display the attention heatmaps generated under the sentence-level setting in this paper. Figure 2 displays the attention heatmaps on MOH and TroFi examples to reflect the influence of metaphorical polarity on the attention scores and Figure 3 contains the heatmaps on LCC examples to show the effect of metaphorical intensities. In Figure 2a, the subject "the good player", the verb "times" and the object "his swing" are all heavily attended, indicating the literal usage of the word "time" paired with the words "player" and "swing". Quite on the contrary, the verb "visited" in Figure 2b is very lightly attended compared to "he" and "illness" in the same sentence, which is a signal of the metaphorical use of the word "visited" in its context. The same pattern applies to the examples in TroFi (Figure 2d and 2c) and LCC (Figure 3a, 3b, 3c and 3d) that the more heavily our model attends on an aspect word, the lower chance it is used metaphorically in the context. It is worth noting that when the sentences grow longer, the amount of potential aspect words also increases. The use of these aspect words can be literal or metaphorical at the same time, which benefits classifying the metaphoricity of the sentence as a whole. In Figure 2a, for instance, the verb "hit" is used literally with the noun "ball" as well. But there are also cases where the multiple aspect words in one sentence hold different metaphoricities, e.g. the words "swallow" and "sink" in Sentence 2 of Table 4. These examples contribute to many prediction errors made by our sentence-level classification model but are generally not a problem for the aspect-based classification and sequential labeling models. As we stated before, examining the metaphoricity of given aspect words only simplifies MD. Given the powerful neural models in the NLP field, we do not need this type of simplification anymore. As our next step, we will keep working on labeling MD datasets at the sentence-level or on the aspect level with multiple aspect words per sentence. We will also introduce social media data to MD for richer metaphorical expressions and varied topics.

8 Conclusion and Future Work

Though difficult, MD has been an important task in the NLP community. In this paper, we refined the definitions of MD by defining a new task formulation. We also designed and evaluated a BERT-based model on three MD benchmark datasets. Our model largely outperformed the previous state-of-the-art methods. Through analysis of the prediction errors made by our model, we found that a large number of prediction errors can be attributed to the simplicity of the datasets and the annotation qualities. To validate this, we re-annotated the MOH dataset and manually verified the quality of our new annotations. We saw in the experiments that our model achieves very high accuracy on existing MD benchmark datasets, meaning that they are becoming overly simple for deep neural networks. Our future work will focus on collecting and annotating a new MD dataset with more complex texts. Regarding the prosperity of social media, we also plan to address the metaphor detection problem on informal text. We hope our work will attract more interest to MD and we call for future contributions to solve the problem.

References

Beata Beigman Klebanov, Chee Wee Leong, E. Dario Gutierrez, Ekaterina Shutova, and Michael Flor. 2016. Semantic classifications for detection of verb metaphors. In *Proceedings of the 54th Annual Meeting of the Association for Computational Linguistics (Volume 2: Short Papers)*, pages 101–106, Berlin, Germany. Association for Computational Linguistics.

Julia Birke and Anoop Sarkar. 2006. A clustering approach for nearly unsupervised recognition of nonliteral language. In *11th Conference of the European Chapter of the Association for Computational Linguistics*, Trento, Italy. Association for Computational Linguistics.

Julia Birke and Anoop Sarkar. 2007. Active learning for the identification of nonliteral language. In *Proceedings of the Workshop on Computational Approaches to Figurative Language*, pages 21–28, Rochester, New York. Association for Computational Linguistics.

David B Bracewell, Marc T Tomlinson, Michael Mohler, and Bryan Rink. 2014. A tiered approach to the recognition of metaphor. In *International Conference on Intelligent Text Processing and Computational Linguistics*, pages 403–414. Springer.

Luana Bulat, Stephen Clark, and Ekaterina Shutova. 2017. Modelling metaphor with attribute-based semantics. In *Proceedings of the 15th Conference of the European Chapter of the Association for Computational Linguistics: Volume 2, Short Papers*, pages 523–528, Valencia, Spain. Association for Computational Linguistics.

Max Coltheart. 1981. The mrc psycholinguistic database. *The Quarterly Journal of Experimental Psychology Section A*, 33(4):497–505.

Verna Dankers, Marek Rei, Martha Lewis, and Ekaterina Shutova. 2019. Modelling the interplay of metaphor and emotion through multitask learning. In *Proceedings of the 2019 Conference on Empirical Methods in Natural Language Processing and the 9th International Joint Conference on Natural Language Processing (EMNLP-IJCNLP)*, pages 2218–2229, Hong Kong, China. Association for Computational Linguistics.

Jacob Devlin, Ming-Wei Chang, Kenton Lee, and Kristina Toutanova. 2019. BERT: Pre-training of deep bidirectional transformers for language understanding. In *Proceedings of the 2019 Conference of the North American Chapter of the Association for Computational Linguistics: Human Language Technologies, Volume 1 (Long and Short Papers)*, pages 4171–4186, Minneapolis, Minnesota. Association for Computational Linguistics.

Erik-Lân Do Dinh and Iryna Gurevych. 2016. Token-level metaphor detection using neural networks. In *Proceedings of the Fourth Workshop on Metaphor in NLP*, pages 28–33, San Diego, California. Association for Computational Linguistics.

Ge Gao, Eunsol Choi, Yejin Choi, and Luke Zettlemoyer. 2018. Neural metaphor detection in context. In *Proceedings of the 2018 Conference on Empirical Methods in Natural Language Processing*, pages 607–613, Brussels, Belgium. Association for Computational Linguistics.

Matt Gedigian, John Bryant, Srini Narayanan, and Branimir Ciric. 2006. Catching metaphors. In *Proceedings of the Third Workshop on Scalable Natural Language Understanding*, pages 41–48, New York City, New York. Association for Computational Linguistics.

Dirk Hovy, Shashank Srivastava, Sujay Kumar Jauhar, Mrinmaya Sachan, Kartik Goyal, Huying Li, Whitney Sanders, and Eduard Hovy. 2013. Identifying metaphorical word use with tree kernels. In *Proceedings of the First Workshop on Metaphor in NLP*, pages 52–57, Atlanta, Georgia. Association for Computational Linguistics.

Hyeju Jang, Yohan Jo, Qinlan Shen, Michael Miller, Seungwhan Moon, and Carolyn Rosé. 2016. Metaphor detection with topic transition, emotion and cognition in context. In *Proceedings of the 54th Annual Meeting of the Association for Computational Linguistics (Volume 1: Long Papers)*, pages 216–225, Berlin, Germany. Association for Computational Linguistics.

G Lakoff and M Johnson. 1980. Metaphors we live by.

George A Miller. 1995. Wordnet: a lexical database for english. *Communications of the ACM*, 38(11):39–41.

George A Miller. 1998. *WordNet: An electronic lexical database*. MIT press.

Saif Mohammad, Ekaterina Shutova, and Peter Turney. 2016. Metaphor as a medium for emotion: An empirical study. In *Proceedings of the Fifth Joint Conference on Lexical and Computational Semantics*, pages 23–33, Berlin, Germany. Association for Computational Linguistics.

Michael Mohler, Mary Brunson, Bryan Rink, and Marc Tomlinson. 2016. Introducing the LCC metaphor datasets. In *Proceedings of the Tenth International Conference on Language Resources and Evaluation (LREC'16)*, pages 4221–4227, Portorož, Slovenia. European Language Resources Association (ELRA).

Matthew Peters, Mark Neumann, Mohit Iyyer, Matt Gardner, Christopher Clark, Kenton Lee, and Luke Zettlemoyer. 2018. Deep contextualized word representations. In *Proceedings of the 2018 Conference of the North American Chapter of the Association for Computational Linguistics: Human Language Technologies, Volume 1 (Long Papers)*, pages 2227–2237, New Orleans, Louisiana. Association for Computational Linguistics.

Marek Rei, Luana Bulat, Douwe Kiela, and Ekaterina Shutova. 2017. Grasping the finer point: A supervised similarity network for metaphor detection. In *Proceedings of the 2017 Conference on Empirical Methods in Natural Language Processing*, pages 1537–1546, Copenhagen, Denmark. Association for Computational Linguistics.

Ekaterina Shutova, Douwe Kiela, and Jean Maillard. 2016. Black holes and white rabbits: Metaphor identification with visual features. In *Proceedings of the 2016 Conference of the North American Chapter of the Association for Computational Linguistics: Human Language Technologies*, pages 160–170, San Diego, California. Association for Computational Linguistics.

Ekaterina Shutova and Lin Sun. 2013. Unsupervised metaphor identification using hierarchical graph factorization clustering. In *Proceedings of the 2013 Conference of the North American Chapter of the Association for Computational Linguistics: Human Language Technologies*, pages 978–988, Atlanta, Georgia. Association for Computational Linguistics.

Ekaterina Shutova, Lin Sun, and Anna Korhonen. 2010. Metaphor identification using verb and noun clustering. In *Proceedings of the 23rd International Conference on Computational Linguistics (Coling 2010)*, pages 1002–1010, Beijing, China. Coling 2010 Organizing Committee.

Gerard Steen. 2010. *A method for linguistic metaphor identification: From MIP to MIPVU*, volume 14. John Benjamins Publishing.

Tomek Strzalkowski, George Aaron Broadwell, Sarah Taylor, Laurie Feldman, Samira Shaikh, Ting Liu, Boris Yamrom, Kit Cho, Umit Boz, Ignacio Cases, and Kyle Elliot. 2013. Robust extraction of metaphor from novel data. In *Proceedings of the First Workshop on Metaphor in NLP*, pages 67–76, Atlanta, Georgia. Association for Computational Linguistics.

Yla R Tausczik and James W Pennebaker. 2010. The psychological meaning of words: Liwc and computerized text analysis methods. *Journal of language and social psychology*, 29(1):24–54.

Yulia Tsvetkov, Leonid Boytsov, Anatole Gershman, Eric Nyberg, and Chris Dyer. 2014. Metaphor detection with cross-lingual model transfer. In *Proceedings of the 52nd Annual Meeting of the Association for Computational Linguistics (Volume 1: Long Papers)*, pages 248–258, Baltimore, Maryland. Association for Computational Linguistics.

Yulia Tsvetkov, Elena Mukomel, and Anatole Gershman. 2013. Cross-lingual metaphor detection using common semantic features. In *Proceedings of the First Workshop on Metaphor in NLP*, pages 45–51, Atlanta, Georgia. Association for Computational Linguistics.

Peter Turney, Yair Neuman, Dan Assaf, and Yohai Cohen. 2011. Literal and metaphorical sense identification through concrete and abstract context. In *Proceedings of the 2011 Conference on Empirical Methods in Natural Language Processing*, pages 680–690, Edinburgh, Scotland, UK. Association for Computational Linguistics.

Michael Wilson. 1988. Mrc psycholinguistic database: Machine-usable dictionary, version 2.00. *Behavior research methods, instruments, & computers*, 20(1):6–10.

Thomas Wolf, Lysandre Debut, Victor Sanh, Julien Chaumond, Clement Delangue, Anthony Moi, Pierric Cistac, Tim Rault, R'emi Louf, Morgan Funtowicz, and Jamie Brew. 2019. Huggingface's transformers: State-of-the-art natural language processing. *ArXiv*, abs/1910.03771.

Human-Model Divergence in the Handling of Vagueness

Elias Stengel-Eskin **Jimena Guallar-Blasco** **Benjamin Van Durme**
Johns Hopkins University
{elias, jguallal, vandurme}@jhu.edu

Abstract

While aggregate performance metrics can generate valuable insights at a large scale, their dominance means more complex and nuanced language phenomena, such as vagueness, may be overlooked. Focusing on vague terms (e.g. *sunny*, *cloudy*, *young*, etc.) we inspect the behavior of visually grounded and text-only models, finding systematic divergences from human judgments even when a model's overall performance is high. To help explain this disparity, we identify two assumptions made by the datasets and models examined and, guided by the philosophy of vagueness, isolate cases where they do not hold.

1 Introduction

Part of the power of language as a medium for communication is rooted in having a reliable mapping between language and the world: we typically expect language to be used in a consistent fashion, i.e. the word "dog" refers to a relatively invariant group of animals, and not to a different set of items each time we use it. This view of language dovetails with the supervised learning paradigm, where we assume that an approximation of such a mapping can be learned from labeled examples—often collected via manual annotation by crowdworkers. In natural language processing (NLP), this learning typically takes place by treating tasks as classification problems which optimize for log-likelihood. While this paradigm has been extensively and successfully applied in NLP, it is not without both practical and theoretical shortcomings. Guided by notions from the philosophy of language, we propose that borderline cases of vague terms, where the mapping between inputs and outputs is unclear, represent an edge case for the assumptions made by the supervised paradigm, and result in systematic divergences between human and model behavior.

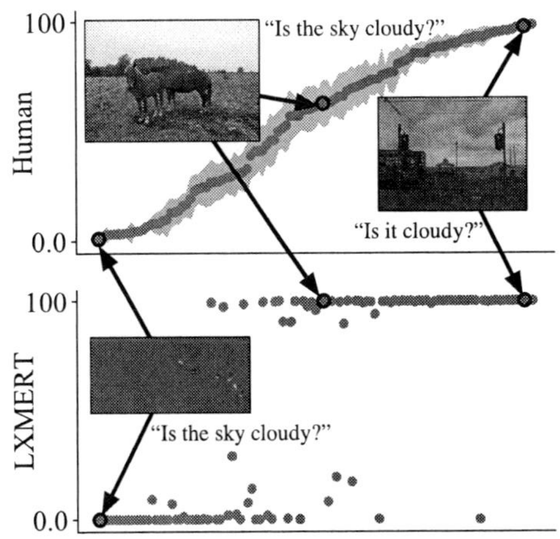

Figure 1: Given a binary question involving a vague term (in this case, *cloudy*) humans hedge between "yes" and "no," following a sigmoid curve with borderline examples falling in the middle. Standard error (grey band) shows that annotator agree even in borderline regions. In contrast, model predictions remain at extreme ends.

To demonstrate this, we begin by identifying a set of canonically vague terms in the binary question subset of the Visual Question Answering (VQA) and GQA datasets (Antol et al., 2015; Goyal et al., 2017; Hudson and Manning, 2019) and isolating a subset of images, questions, and answers from these datasets centered around these terms. Using this subset, we show that while the accuracy of LXMERT (Tan and Bansal, 2019) on non-borderline cases is very high, its performance drops—sometimes dramatically—on borderline cases. We then compare the behavior of the model against that of human annotators, finding that while humans display behavior which aligns with theories of meaning for vague terms, model behavior is less predictable.

We extend our analysis of visually-grounded terms to a text-only case, re-framing the catego-

Proceedings of the 1st Workshop on Understanding Implicit and Underspecified Language (UnImplicit 2021), pages 43–57
Bangkok, Thailand (online), August 5, 2021.

rization of statements into true statements and false ones as a task involving vagueness. Controlling for world knowledge, we find that while probes over contextualized encoders can classify statements significantly better than random, their output distributions are strikingly similar to those observed in the visually-grounded case. When contrasted with scalar annotations collected from crowdworkers, these results support the notion that analytic truth itself admits of borderline cases and poses problems for supervised systems.

In § 2, we provide a more thorough definition of terms used, the motivation for exploring vagueness, and the underlying assumptions of supervised learning that are violated by vague terms.

2 Motivation and Background

Vague terms, broadly speaking, are ones that admit of borderline cases; for example: *cloudy* is vague because, while there are clearly cloudy and not cloudy days, there are also cases where the best response to the question "is it cloudy?" might be "somewhat" rather than a definitive "yes" or "no." Given this definition, we can see that a large portion of the predicates we use in every-day speech are vague. This even encompasses predicates such as *is true* and *is false*, as we might have statements that are true or false to varying degrees.

Vague predicates in particular have been a focus of the philosophy of language, as they represent an interesting edge case for theories of meaning. Take, for example, a canonical example of a vague predicate from philosophy: *is a heap*. There are things that are undeniable heaps, and others that are clearly not. In the extreme case, we can imagine starting with a heap of sand (say, N grains) and removing a single grain of sand from it. Clearly, the resulting mass would still be a heap. This is, however, a dangerous precedent; we can now remove $N-2$ grains on sand until we have a single grain remaining, whose heap-ness is hard to justify, but which, by induction, is still a heap. This raises important questions: how is it that speakers avoid this paradox and are able to use and understand vague terms, even in borderline cases? Is there a definitive point at which a heap becomes a non-heap? The answers to these questions should influence how we annotate the data from which we aim to learn meaning representations of vague terms.

While the unequivocal instances of heaps fit well into the current paradigm of supervised learning with categorical labels, borderline heaps do present a problem. Recall that the first assumption by supervised learning which we have pointed out is that the ideal mapping between the input (in this case, questions and images) and the the label set (answers) is largely fixed. For example, given the question "Is this a dog?" we assume that the set of things in the world which we call "dog", also known as the *extension* of "dog", remains constant. In that case, the annotator's response to the question corresponds to whether what the image depicts could be plausibly considered as part of the extension of "dog." While we might easily be able to determine the set membership of poodles and terriers, we may have a harder time with Jack London's White Fang: half wolf, half dog. Thus it is clear that the borderline cases of vague terms demand a more nuanced account than merely a forced choice between two extremes. The range of such accounts fall broadly into three classes:

Contextualist theories (Kamp, 1981; Raffman, 1994; Graff, 2000; Shapiro, 2006, i.a.) broadly hold that the interpretation of vague predicates depend on contextual and pragmatic information such as on the speaker's previous commitments, their perceived goals, and the psychological state of the interpreter. This view could in most cases be reconciled with the supervised learning paradigm, provided that the data upon which the interpretation of the vague predicate hinges (i.e. speaker commitments, etc.) is available as input. Past work in modeling the meaning of vague terms has often focused on these accounts (c.f. § 6).

Epistemic accounts (Sorensen, 2001; Williamson, 1994, i.a.) bite the proverbial bullet, allowing for a hard boundary between heaps and non-heaps to exist, but claiming that its location is unknowable. This is in contrast to the supervised paradigm, where the boundary is treated as known.

Logic-based approaches tackle the paradox induced by vagueness, either by claiming that borderline examples do not admit of truth values (supervaluationism), or by adapting logic to permit more granular classifications (many-valued logic; Sorensen, 2018). The latter approach can sometimes accommodate the supervised paradigm.[1]

[1]It may still be incompatible with log-likelihood. Treating *ordinal* many-valued logic as a k-way classification problem requires that all values be equidistant, i.e. predicting a value of 1/5 when the true value is 4/5 is as bad as rating it 3/5.

Ambiguity and Under-specification It is important to distinguish vagueness from under-specification (imprecision in the input making the output difficult to recover) and ambiguity (the presence of multiple valid answers), both alternative explanations for annotator disagreement. Indeed, Bhattacharya et al. (2019) include both in their taxonomy of VQA images-question pairs with high annotator disagreement. While they are major challenges in any language-based task, both are often defeasible in nature: we can provide additional information that would reveal the "correct" answer to an annotator, i.e. we could provide a better, sharper version of the image, or more contextual information. Vagueness is non-defeasible: even if one were to know the exact number of grains of sand, the predicate "*is a heap*" would remain vague.

3 Visually Grounded Vagueness

The interpretation of vague terms as described in § 1 typically occurs in a grounded setting; the question "Is this a dog?" is only meaningful in the context of some state of affairs (or depiction thereof). We focus on binary questions about images, taking examples from VQA and GQA; this ensures that the vague term is the question's focus, excluding open-ended queries like "What is the old man doing?" which only implicitly involve vagueness.

Data collection We begin by isolating a number of vague descriptors (*sunny*, *cloudy*, *adult*, *young*, *new*, *old*) in the VQA and GQA datasets. We then use high-recall regular expressions to match questions from these descriptors in the development sets of both datasets, manually filtering the results to obtain high-precision examples. Here, we make the simplifying assumption that a group of predicates involving these terms, such as "is *x*", "seems *x*" and "looks *x*" are approximately equivalent and used interchangeably.

This process results in a variable number of questions per descriptor, with *sunny* and *cloudy* typically having far more representation. Given the size of the whole development sets, and the fact that the data presented is being used merely for analysis rather than for training models, we annotate between 32 and 264 examples, depending on the data availability for each predicate.[2]

While the VQA development data contains 10 annotations per example, GQA does not, and thus, in order to verify the quality of the VQA annotations and to collect annotations for GQA, we solicited 10-way redundant annotations from Mechanical Turk, presenting annotators with a question and its corresponding image from the vision-and-language dataset (e.g. "Is it sunny?").[3] Rather than providing categorical labels (e.g. "yes", "no") workers were asked to use a slider bar ranging from "no" to "yes", whose values range from 0 to 100, using an interface inspired by Sakaguchi and Van Durme (2018). Examples were provided in groups of 8.[4] The resulting annotations are normalized per annotator by the following formula $x' = (x - x_{\text{min}})/x_{\text{max}}$ where x_{min} and x_{max} are the annotators minimum and maximum scores. This accounts for differences in slider bar usage by different annotators. Inter-annotator agreement is measured via majority voting, where an annotator is said to agree with others when their judgement falls on the same side of the slider bar scale (i.e. > 50, < 50). Using this metric, we exclude annotators with $< 75\%$ agreement. After exclusion, all predicates had $> 90\%$ average agreement.[5].

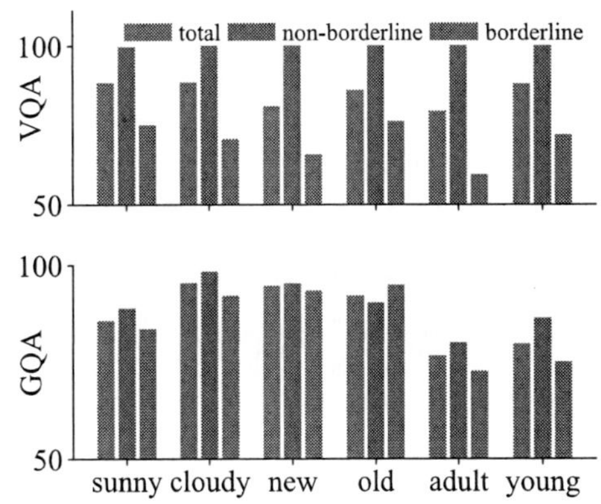

Figure 2: Accuracy of LXMERT on VQA and GQA Yes/No questions per predicate is highest for non-borderline examples, but drops in "borderline" regions.

Vagueness and accuracy We begin by demonstrating that vagueness is not merely a theoretical problem: Fig. 2 shows that while the total accuracy of LXMERT (Tan and Bansal, 2019) is fairly high, it drops on all descriptors (except for "old" for GQA) when looking only at accuracy in the borderline regions. For VQA, we take advantage of the

[2]Note that for some predicates (e.g. *sunny* and *cloudy*, more data was available.

[3]Since we were merely verifying the data quality for VQA, we only ran two descriptors: "sunny" and "cloudy".

[4]c.f. Appendix A for more on the collection protocol.

[5]All data is available at `website.com`

existing 10-way redundant annotations, defining borderline examples as those for which there was any disagreement between annotators, i.e. even if 9 annotators responded "yes" and one responded "no" for a given example, it is considered borderline. This results in 49.24% borderline cases. We find that for GQA, defining borderline examples as having mean normalized scores $\in [15.0, 85.0]$ yields roughly the same percentage (47.20% borderline).

The contrast between borderline and non-borderline regions is especially dramatic for VQA, with the minimum non-borderline accuracy being 99.67% for "sunny," while the accuracy in the borderline region drops to 69.78%. Though the results are less dramatic for GQA, they generally trend in the same direction. We argue that, given that these borderline examples account for roughly half of the data examined, the relatively high aggregate performance obtained by models on binary questions in VQA and GQA may be partially attributed to an absence of vague terms rather than to the strength of the model. Conversely, given a shifted evaluation dataset with more vague terms, the performance would likely drop dramatically.

Vagueness in detail Having demonstrated that model performance is diminished on borderline cases, we seek to further explore the divergence in model and human behavior.

Fig. 1 plots the mean human scores in the top plot, with examples ordered by their mean human rating. The bottom plot shows LXMERT output scores for the same examples. The human scores display a sigmoid shape, while the model scores are saturated at either 0 or 1. For the sake of space, the remaining plots are reported in Appendix B, and we constrain ourselves to a quantitative analysis to demonstrate that a similar trend holds across the remaining descriptors.

Following Item Response Theory (Reise et al., 2005; Lalor et al., 2016) – a modeling paradigm for psychological tests premised on variability among respondents – we posit a 2-parameter sigmoid response function given by $\big(1 + \exp\big(-k * (x - x_0)\big)\big)^{-1}$ where k and x_0 are scale and shift parameters, respectively. This parameterization reflects the intuition that non-borderline examples are found near the spectrum's ends (0 and 100) while borderline examples form a curve in the spectrum's center. In other words, it defines an "ideal" curve in the sigmoid family that fits the data collected from annotators. In some cases, this curve is stretched, nearing a line, while in others it is more pronounced.

We fit three separate logistic regressions: one to the mean of the annotator responses, one to the model response obtained from LXMERT, and a baseline fit against data drawn from a uniform distribution. The quality of the fit, measured by root mean squared error (RMSE) on 10% held-out data, repeated across 10 folds of cross-validation, is given in Fig. 3. For both datasets, sigmoid functions fit to model predictions have an RMSE comparable to those fit to uniformly random data, while the functions fit to human data have errors an order of magnitude lower.

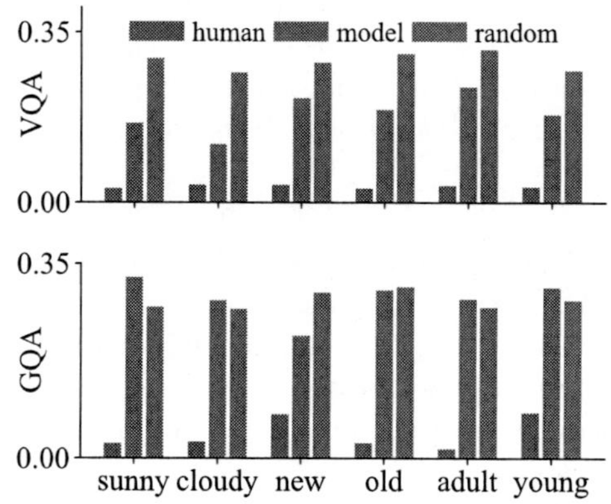

Figure 3: Mean RMSE from sigmoid fit to VQA and GQA data using 10-fold cross-validation. Human predictions result in a far better sigmoid fit, while model predictions have similar fit to data $\sim \mathcal{U}(0, 1)$.

This indicates that the remaining GQA and VQA predicates follow a similar pattern to the one seen in Fig. 1. While model predictions often fall on the correct side of the middle threshold, as examples become borderline, some predictions become erratic while others are confidently misclassified. Note that this is doubly problematic: firstly, the model only makes use of a small region of the label space. While the output vocabulary includes entries such as "partly cloudy" and "overcast," for all examples tested, the model assigns $> 98\%$ of its probability mass to "yes" and "no."

Even within this constrained assignment, the model has the possibility of hedging using the output logits (e.g. $p(\text{yes}|x) = 0.40$ etc.). *Prima facie* we might hope that, given a large categorically-labeled dataset, the model would learn the correct output distribution, as Pavlick and Kwiatkowski (2019) put it, "for free." We do not find this to be the case: the prediction generally heavily favors one label alone, posing problems for any downstream task as well as active learning setups using uncertainty sampling (Lewis and Catlett, 1994).

In contrast, annotators display hedging between the labels, reliably using the slider-bar interface to equivocate between extremes in borderline cases. These results suggest that the first assumption described in § 2, namely that images can be identified as being in the extension of a descriptor or not (e.g. in the set of scenes described as "cloudy"), holds only at the ends of the example range, and is not warranted in the borderline region. In contrast, the training data which LXMERT sees makes the assumption that the descriptor either applies (examples with a "yes" label) or does not apply (examples labelled "no") in all regions; we see that this is perhaps too strong of an assumption when trying to capture the nuances of vague terms.

Note also that the annotators' standard error (grey band) is generally fairly low even in the central region, where we would expect greater disagreement. This trend holds across descriptors, and perhaps implies that the second assumption, that annotators can reliably recover the mapping between inputs and outputs, does to hold as long as the annotators are provided the proper interface for expressing their intuitions.

4 Text-only Vagueness

§ 3 explored predicates grounded in another representation of the world, namely images. However, much of NLP deals with text in isolation, without grounding to some external modality. In an ungrounded setting, it is unproductive to evaluate models on external knowledge that they would not have access to—thus, we cannot evaluate a text-only model's performance on vague predicates the same way as a grounded model's performance. In other words, we need to develop a paradigm which does not rely on knowledge about a state of the world, but rather on linguistic knowledge. This is precisely the analytic-synthetic distinction, with analytic truths being truths *by virtue of meaning alone* (e.g. "a bachelor is an unmarried man") and synthetic truths being those which require verification against a state of affairs (e.g. "Garfield is a bachelor"). To avoid evaluating our text-only models on their ability to reason against a world which they are not privy to, we restrict our analysis to analytic truths and falsehoods, which we construct by pairing words either with their true definition or with a distractor definition, creating statements that are analytically true and false. Recall from § 2 that

Sentence	T/F	Mark
journalism is newspapers and magazines collectively	T	◇
T-shirt is an archaic term for clothing	F	△
T-shirt is a close-fitting pullover shirt	T	●
a teammate is someone who is under suspicion	F	■

Table 1: Example sentences, with their label in the created dataset and corresponding color in Fig. 4.

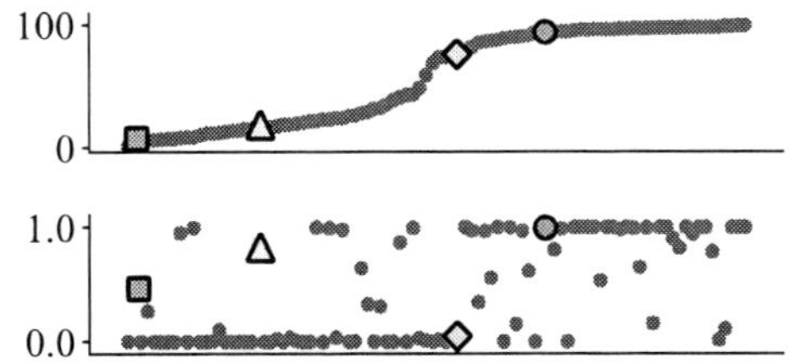

Figure 4: *Top:* mean truth score given by humans on 96 statements. False statements colored red, true blue; statements from Table 1 overlaid. *Bottom:* $P(\text{true})$ assigned by the best probing classifier (XLNet + [CLS]).

even the predicates *is true* and *is false* may be seen as vague; there are statements which are only partially true or false, and we can speak meaningfully of some statements being truer than others.

Following Ettinger et al. (2018), these statements are created artificially, mitigating annotator bias. Definitions of the 2542 most frequent English nouns[6] are then obtained from WordNet (Miller, 1995; Fellbaum, 1998) using the NLTK interface (Bird, 2006). By pairing a "trigger" word with its definition, we create an analytically true statement (c.f. row 3 in Table 1). In order to create analytically false statements, we pair the same word with a definition for a related but distinct term. A set of candidate terms is created recursively taking the hypernym of the trigger word's top wordsense[7] for three levels (i.e. the hyper-hyper-hypernym) and adding all its hyponyms, excluding the trigger's siblings. The best distractor candidate is chosen using lexical overlap, where the candidate with the lowest overlap with the true definition is chosen. Note that as a simplifying assumption we ignore polysemy here; it is possible that via polysemy the

[6] https://www.wordfrequency.info

[7] Based on pilot evaluations, we exclude chemistry-related wordsenses, as their definitions often contain low-frequency technical terms.

chosen distractor definition is not strictly analytically false. However, this result is unlikely given that human annotators reliably recognized distractor definitions. We expect that, while the examples are categorically labeled *true* and *false*, annotators will determine that certain statements fall into a borderline region between these extremes, corresponding to notions like "partially true" or "mostly false."[8] Crucially, where in § 3 the vagueness was present in the question itself (i.e. the task was to determine whether the object in question, e.g. the sky, in the image fell into the extension of the vague term e.g. things that are cloudy) here it is in the label set; the task becomes determining whether the statement as a whole falls into the set of true statements. The data is split into 4000 train, 500 development, and 536 test sentences. For all triggers, both statements are found in the same split.

96 sentences were sampled from the development set and annotated with 10-way redundancy by vetted crowdworkers on Mechanical Turk. Using a similar interface as in § 3, annotators were presented with sentences and asked to rate the sentence's truth using a sliding bar (ranging from 0 to 100) from false to true. In addition, an "I don't know" checkbox was provided to avoid forcing a choice. Sentences were presented in groups of 8. Additional details on the annotation interface can be found in Appendix A.

4.1 Encoders and Models

While the text-only experiments also focus on examining vagueness, several important contrasts to § 3 must be drawn. In the visual setting, the entire LXMERT model was separately finetuned on the whole GQA and VQA train splits, and analysis examples were sourced from the development data. In the text-only case, we do not have a pre-made dataset and construct our own. Due to the smaller size of our dataset, we have opted to only fine-tune the classification layer, freezing the weights of the contextualized encoders, unlike in the visual setting where we trained the entire model. This is far less computationally expensive, and allows us to expand our text-only analysis to a range of encoder types and model architectures. We examine three different contextualized encoders:

BERT BERT (Devlin et al., 2019) is a transformer-based model which uses a word's context to predict its identity; during training, words in the input are randomly replaced with a `[MASK]` token; the model then predicts masked words based on their contexts—a cloze-style task known as masked language modeling (MLM). BERT also uses a next-sentence prediction objective.

RoBERTa RoBERTa (Liu et al., 2019) uses roughly the same methodology as BERT, but trains the model for more epochs with larger batch sizes while removing the next-sentence prediction task.

XLNet While traditional language models only consider one factorization (in the forwards or the backwards direction), Yang et al. (2019) maximize the expected log-likelihood with respect to all factorizations input's joint probability.

Drawing on the observations of Warstadt et al. (2019) that probing results can change dramatically depending on how an encoder is probed, we introduce three probing classifiers:

Mean-pool The mean-pool classifier takes the average across all dimensions of the encoder output at each input token, yielding one vector for the whole sentence. This vector is then passed to a 2-layer multi-layer perceptron (MLP) with ReLU activations, which produces a classification over the 2D output space.

Sequence The sequence classifier uses the encoder representation at the index of the `[CLS]` token, which it then passes to a 2-layer MLP with twice as many hidden units as input units.

Bilinear This classifier splits the probing prompt into a trigger word (e.g. "bachelor") and a definition (e.g. "an unmarried man"); it encodes both into vectors, mean-pooling the definition to produce two vectors, which are projected through two linear layers. The projected representations x_{trig} and x_{def} are then passed through a bilinear layer, given by $f(x_{\text{trig}}, x_{\text{def}}) = x_{\text{trig}}^T \mathbf{A}\, x_{\text{def}}$, where $\mathbf{A}$ is a 3-dimensional learned parameter.

Control Tasks Following Hewitt and Liang (2019), we construct control tasks for all of our models and encoders. A control task is one where labels and inputs are paired randomly; the purpose of such a task is to disentangle what portion of the probing classifier's performance can be attributed to the strength of the classifier, and what portion is present in the representation.[9]

[8]Note that this conceptualization of truth diverges from that of classical logic, but may be more faithful to actual usage.

[9]All models are trained for 100 epochs with the Adam optimizer using a learning rate of 0.0001. The best model was chosen by validation performance.

5 Results and Analysis

We find that our control classifiers perform randomly, indicating our task has very low sensitivity. Fig. 5 shows the test accuracies of all (non-control) models in all settings. We see that all models fall well below human performance, but well above the random baseline of 50%. Among the probing methods, `[CLS]` pooling slightly outperforms mean-pooling. The bilinear method consistently underperforms the pooling methods, suggesting that the gap between human and model performance is not due to malformed prompts (e.g. incorrect articles in the definition or trigger phrase). Appendix C gives some examples and model predictions.

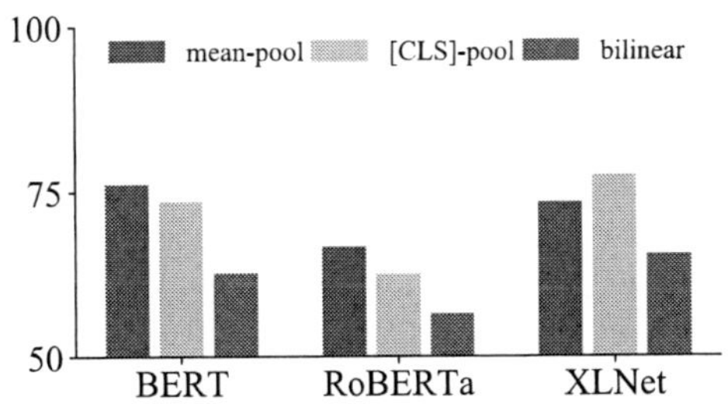

Figure 5: Test accuracy across encoders and probing methods; all models perform well above chance.

Human annotators are able to perform the task with high reliability, achieving an accuracy of 88.54 with majority voting. Fig. 4 shows that certain sentences are easily classified as either true or false, while a smaller number of sentences are considered borderline. A qualitative analysis of these sentences reveals that they typically fall into two categories: sentences where the trigger described is very abstract (e.g. "a separation is the state of lacking unity") and those where the distractor definition is very closely related to the trigger (e.g. "a baby is a person's brother or sister"). Intuitively, both of these phenomena can make a sentence only partially true or false.

While Fig. 5 suggests the models are performing reasonably well in the aggregate, Fig. 4 demonstrates a similar trend to those seen in § 3, showing that the classification patterns of humans differ drastically from those of the best model, as illustrated by the overlaid examples. We also see the same overconfidence in the output distribution of the model, with predictions saturating at either end of the simplex. Fig. 6 further reinforces this; here, we perform the same analysis as in § 3, fit-

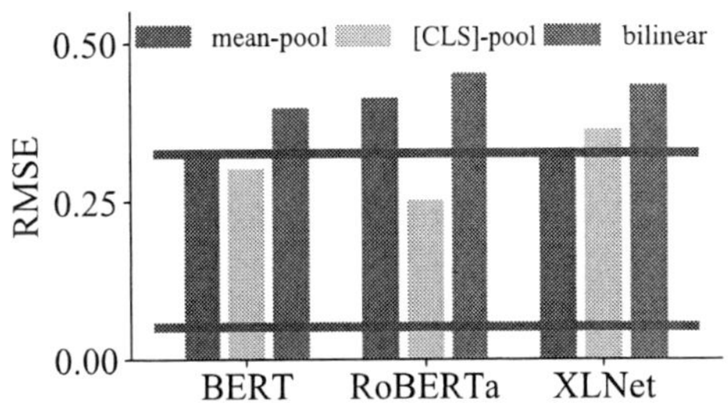

Figure 6: 10-fold cross-validated RMSE against model of 2-parameter sigmoid against model predictions from each encoder and model pairing. RMSE to human performance (green line, bottom) and against random data (red line, top) are overlaid. RMSE to model predictions is close to or worse than to random data.

ting a 2-parameter logistic regression to the aggregate human scores, the model predictions, and samples of a uniformly-distributed random variable, computing the RMSE between the best-fit sigmoid and the data. Across all models and all encoder types, we see that the RMSE of a sigmoid fit to the model predictions is close to or higher than the RMSE of a sigmoid fit to uniformly random data ($\text{RMSE}_{\text{random}} = 0.326$), as evidenced by the overlaid red horizontal line, while the sigmoid fit to human performance has a far lower RSME ($\text{RMSE}_{\text{human}} = 0.051$). This quantitatively reinforces the qualitative difference seen in Fig. 4.

6 Related Work

Human-model divergence In similar vein to our work, Pavlick and Kwiatkowski (2019) observe that human annotators consistently disagree on natural language inference (NLI) labels, and that the disagreement cannot be attributed to a lack of annotations. They similarly find that models do not implicitly learn to capture human uncertainty from categorical data. In contrast, our work seeks to pinpoint vagueness as a cause for some of the difference in behavior.[10]

Other work has looked at annotating data to accommodate the kinds of disagreements seen in Pavlick and Kwiatkowski. Chen et al. (2020) extends the EASL framework (Sakaguchi and Van Durme, 2018) for efficiently eliciting reliable scalar judgements from crowdworkers to NLI, ob-

[10]We examined high-disagreement examples from the data released by Pavlick and Kwiatkowski, which largely seem not to be caused by vagueness except for some examples from JOCI (Zhang et al., 2017), e.g. *P*: "I loved apple sauce", *H*: "The sauce is a condiment" may have high disagreement due to vagueness in the predicate *isACondiment(x)*".

taining scalar NLI judgements rather than categorical labels. In a similar context, Li et al. (2019) argue that for tasks involving plausibility, the use of cross-entropy loss drives model predictions to the extremes of the simplex, and demonstrate the benefits of shifting to a margin-based loss on the Choice of Plausible Alternatives (Roemmele et al., 2011) task. These results dovetail with our observations regarding various models' output distributions, especially in the text-only setting, where our task is very similar to tasks measuring plausibility.

While Pavlick and Kwiatkowski (2019) focus on NLI data, Bhattacharya et al. (2019) have noted that similar disagreements exist in the visual domain, specifically on the VQA data set, where they find that certain image-question pairs are less reliably answered than others. The ontology they propose to classify these images includes ambiguity and under-specification, but not vagueness.

Vagueness Past work in vagueness has often focused on modeling it as a phenomenon, while our work is concerned with analyzing model performance on vague predicates, rather than capturing the semantics of vague predicates, which has been the focus of previous work such as Meo et al. (2014) and McMahan and Stone (2015). Although color terms provide a particularly rich substrate for modeling the semantics of vague terms, we have chosen to exclude them as we feel they demand a level of psychophysical analysis beyond the scope of this work. This work deals instead with gradable terms, following work such as Fernández and Larsson (2014), who present a type-theory record account of vagueness for learning the semantics of gradable adjectives, DeVault and Stone (2004), who use vagueness to illustrate the need for context in a dialog-driven drawing task, and Lassiter and Goodman (2017), who introduce a Bayesian pragmatic model of gradable adjective usage. These lines of previous work draw on the contextualist account of vagueness, holding that the meaning of vague predicates shifts with respect to the interests of the parties communicating, a notion that naturally expresses itself in rational pragmatic models of dialog. Rather than modeling vagueness, we use it as a tool to examine model behavior, focusing on single interactions instead of a dialog. We refer the reader to Juhl and Loomis (2009) for a full account of the analytic/synthetic distinction.

Text-only semantic probing The challenge of analyzing the semantic content of sentence encodings precedes the contextual encoders studied herein; Ettinger et al. (2016) introduce a suite of simple classification tasks for probing the compositionality of LSTM-based sentence embeddings, while Conneau et al. (2018) present 10 linguistically-motivated probing tasks, including 3 semantic tasks, for LSTM- and CNN-based sentence embeddings. Ettinger et al. (2018) create a set of artificial prompts, as done in this work, to probe the compositionality of InferSent (Conneau et al., 2017), while Dasgupta et al. (2018) use NLI-style prompts for the same purpose.

Similar probing suites have been proposed since the advent of contextual encoders; Tenney et al. (2019b) propose a set of edge-probing tasks that examine semantic content, and Tenney et al. (2019a) find that semantic information is typically encoded at higher transformer layers. Presenting a suite of negative polarity item-based tasks, Warstadt et al. (2019) expand on the observation that different transformer layers account for different phenomena, noting that additionally, the manner in which a probing task is framed often makes a large impact.

Dictionary Embeddings Dictionary embeddings, as described by Hill et al. (2016), use dictionary resources to learn a mapping from phrases to word vectors. Dictionaries have also been used with a view to augmenting the semantic information in word embeddings, as in Tissier et al. (2017) and Bosc and Vincent (2018). In contrast to these approaches, we use definitions to investigate the semantic content of existing mappings.

7 Conclusion

We have identified clashes between the assumptions made under the current NLP paradigm and the realities of language use by focusing on the phenomenon of vagueness. By isolating a subset of examples from VQA and GQA involving vagueness, we were able to pinpoint some key divergences between model and human behavior which result in lower model performance. We then created an artificial text-only dataset, controlling for world knowledge, which we used to contrast multiple models building on multiple contextualized encoders, finding similar human-model contrasts. In closing, we would like to advocate for the broader use of concepts from the philosophy of language, such as vagueness, in challenging current models and providing additional insights beyond aggregate statistics and leaderboards.

References

Stanislaw Antol, Aishwarya Agrawal, Jiasen Lu, Margaret Mitchell, Dhruv Batra, C. Lawrence Zitnick, and Devi Parikh. 2015. VQA: Visual Question Answering. In *International Conference on Computer Vision (ICCV)*.

Nilavra Bhattacharya, Qing Li, and Danna Gurari. 2019. Why does a visual question have different answers? In *Proceedings of the IEEE International Conference on Computer Vision*, pages 4271–4280.

Steven Bird. 2006. Nltk: the natural language toolkit. In *Proceedings of the COLING/ACL on Interactive presentation sessions*, pages 69–72. Association for Computational Linguistics.

Tom Bosc and Pascal Vincent. 2018. Auto-encoding dictionary definitions into consistent word embeddings. In *Proceedings of the 2018 Conference on Empirical Methods in Natural Language Processing*, pages 1522–1532.

Tongfei Chen, Zhengping Jiang, Adam Poliak, Keisuke Sakaguchi, and Benjamin Van Durme. 2020. Uncertain natural language inference. In *Proceedings of the 58th Annual Meeting of the Association for Computational Linguistics*, pages 8772–8779, Online. Association for Computational Linguistics.

Alexis Conneau, Douwe Kiela, Holger Schwenk, Loïc Barrault, and Antoine Bordes. 2017. Supervised learning of universal sentence representations from natural language inference data. In *Proceedings of the 2017 Conference on Empirical Methods in Natural Language Processing*, pages 670–680, Copenhagen, Denmark. Association for Computational Linguistics.

Alexis Conneau, German Kruszewski, Guillaume Lample, Loïc Barrault, and Marco Baroni. 2018. What you can cram into a single &!#* vector: Probing sentence embeddings for linguistic properties. In *ACL 2018-56th Annual Meeting of the Association for Computational Linguistics*, volume 1, pages 2126–2136. Association for Computational Linguistics.

Ishita Dasgupta, Demi Guo, Andreas Stuhlmüller, Samuel J Gershman, and Noah D Goodman. 2018. Evaluating compositionality in sentence embeddings. *arXiv preprint arXiv:1802.04302*.

David DeVault and Matthew Stone. 2004. Interpreting vague utterances in context. In *COLING 2004: Proceedings of the 20th International Conference on Computational Linguistics*, pages 1247–1253.

Jacob Devlin, Ming-Wei Chang, Kenton Lee, and Kristina Toutanova. 2019. Bert: Pre-training of deep bidirectional transformers for language understanding. In *Proceedings of the 2019 Conference of the North American Chapter of the Association for Computational Linguistics: Human Language Technologies, Volume 1 (Long and Short Papers)*, pages 4171–4186.

Allyson Ettinger, Ahmed Elgohary, Colin Phillips, and Philip Resnik. 2018. Assessing composition in sentence vector representations. In *Proceedings of the 27th International Conference on Computational Linguistics*, pages 1790–1801.

Allyson Ettinger, Ahmed Elgohary, and Philip Resnik. 2016. Probing for semantic evidence of composition by means of simple classification tasks. In *Proceedings of the 1st Workshop on Evaluating Vector-Space Representations for NLP*, pages 134–139, Berlin, Germany. Association for Computational Linguistics.

Christiane Fellbaum. 1998. Wordnet: An electronic lexical database cambridge. *MA: MIT Press*.

Raquel Fernández and Staffan Larsson. 2014. Vagueness and learning: A type-theoretic approach. In *Proceedings of the Third Joint Conference on Lexical and Computational Semantics (* SEM 2014)*, pages 151–159.

Yash Goyal, Tejas Khot, Douglas Summers-Stay, Dhruv Batra, and Devi Parikh. 2017. Making the V in VQA matter: Elevating the role of image understanding in Visual Question Answering. In *Conference on Computer Vision and Pattern Recognition (CVPR)*.

Delia Graff. 2000. Shifting sands: An interest-relative theory of vagueness. *Philosophical topics*, 28(1):45–81.

John Hewitt and Percy Liang. 2019. Designing and interpreting probes with control tasks. In *Proceedings of the 2019 Conference on Empirical Methods in Natural Language Processing and the 9th International Joint Conference on Natural Language Processing (EMNLP-IJCNLP)*, pages 2733–2743.

Felix Hill, Kyunghyun Cho, Anna Korhonen, and Yoshua Bengio. 2016. Learning to understand phrases by embedding the dictionary. *Transactions of the Association for Computational Linguistics*, 4:17–30.

Drew A Hudson and Christopher D Manning. 2019. Gqa: A new dataset for real-world visual reasoning and compositional question answering. In *Proceedings of the IEEE Conference on Computer Vision and Pattern Recognition*, pages 6700–6709.

Cory Juhl and Eric Loomis. 2009. *Analyticity*. Routledge.

Hans Kamp. 1981. The paradox of the heap. In *Aspects of Philosophical Logic*, pages 225–277. Springer.

John P. Lalor, Hao Wu, and Hong Yu. 2016. Building an evaluation scale using item response theory. In *Proceedings of the 2016 Conference on Empirical Methods in Natural Language Processing*, pages 648–657, Austin, Texas. Association for Computational Linguistics.

Daniel Lassiter and Noah D Goodman. 2017. Adjectival vagueness in a bayesian model of interpretation. *Synthese*, 194(10):3801–3836.

David D Lewis and Jason Catlett. 1994. Heterogeneous uncertainty sampling for supervised learning. In *Machine learning proceedings 1994*, pages 148–156. Elsevier.

Zhongyang Li, Tongfei Chen, and Benjamin Van Durme. 2019. Learning to rank for plausible plausibility. In *Proceedings of the 57th Annual Meeting of the Association for Computational Linguistics*, pages 4818–4823.

Yinhan Liu, Myle Ott, Naman Goyal, Jingfei Du, Mandar Joshi, Danqi Chen, Omer Levy, Mike Lewis, Luke Zettlemoyer, and Veselin Stoyanov. 2019. Roberta: A robustly optimized bert pretraining approach. *arXiv preprint arXiv:1907.11692*.

Brian McMahan and Matthew Stone. 2015. A bayesian model of grounded color semantics. *Transactions of the Association for Computational Linguistics*, 3:103–115.

Timothy Meo, Brian McMahan, and Matthew Stone. 2014. Generating and resolving vague color references. In *Proceedings of the 18th Workshop on the Semantics and Pragmatics of Dialogue (SemDial)*, pages 107–115.

George A Miller. 1995. Wordnet: a lexical database for english. *Communications of the ACM*, 38(11):39–41.

Ellie Pavlick and Tom Kwiatkowski. 2019. Inherent disagreements in human textual inferences. *Transactions of the Association for Computational Linguistics*, 7:677–694.

Diana Raffman. 1994. Vagueness without paradox. *The Philosophical Review*, 103(1):41–74.

Steven P. Reise, Andrew T. Ainsworth, and Mark G. Haviland. 2005. Item response theory: Fundamentals, applications, and promise in psychological research. *Current Directions in Psychological Science*, 14(2):95–101.

Melissa Roemmele, Cosmin Adrian Bejan, and Andrew S Gordon. 2011. Choice of plausible alternatives: An evaluation of commonsense causal reasoning. In *AAAI spring symposium: logical formalizations of commonsense reasoning*, pages 90–95.

Keisuke Sakaguchi and Benjamin Van Durme. 2018. Efficient online scalar annotation with bounded support. In *Proceedings of the 56th Annual Meeting of the Association for Computational Linguistics (Volume 1: Long Papers)*, pages 208–218.

Stewart Shapiro. 2006. *Vagueness in context*. Oxford University Press on Demand.

Roy Sorensen. 2001. *Vagueness and contradiction*. Clarendon Press.

Roy Sorensen. 2018. Vagueness. In Edward N. Zalta, editor, *The Stanford Encyclopedia of Philosophy*, summer 2018 edition. Metaphysics Research Lab, Stanford University.

Hao Tan and Mohit Bansal. 2019. Lxmert: Learning cross-modality encoder representations from transformers. In *Proceedings of the 2019 Conference on Empirical Methods in Natural Language Processing and the 9th International Joint Conference on Natural Language Processing (EMNLP-IJCNLP)*, pages 5103–5114.

Ian Tenney, Dipanjan Das, and Ellie Pavlick. 2019a. BERT rediscovers the classical NLP pipeline. In *Proceedings of the 57th Annual Meeting of the Association for Computational Linguistics*, pages 4593–4601, Florence, Italy. Association for Computational Linguistics.

Ian Tenney, Patrick Xia, Berlin Chen, Alex Wang, Adam Poliak, R Thomas McCoy, Najoung Kim, Benjamin Van Durme, Sam Bowman, Dipanjan Das, and Ellie Pavlick. 2019b. What do you learn from context? probing for sentence structure in contextualized word representations. In *International Conference on Learning Representations*.

Julien Tissier, Christopher Gravier, and Amaury Habrard. 2017. Dict2vec: Learning word embeddings using lexical dictionaries. In *Proceedings of the 2017 Conference on Empirical Methods in Natural Language Processing*, pages 254–263.

Alex Warstadt, Yu Cao, Ioana Grosu, Wei Peng, Hagen Blix, Yining Nie, Anna Alsop, Shikha Bordia, Haokun Liu, Alicia Parrish, et al. 2019. Investigating bert's knowledge of language: Five analysis methods with npis. In *Proceedings of the 2019 Conference on Empirical Methods in Natural Language Processing and the 9th International Joint Conference on Natural Language Processing (EMNLP-IJCNLP)*, pages 2870–2880.

Timothy Williamson. 1994. *Vagueness*. Routledge.

Zhilin Yang, Zihang Dai, Yiming Yang, Jaime Carbonell, Ruslan Salakhutdinov, and Quoc V Le. 2019. Xlnet: Generalized autoregressive pretraining for language understanding. *arXiv preprint arXiv:1906.08237*.

Sheng Zhang, Rachel Rudinger, Kevin Duh, and Benjamin Van Durme. 2017. Ordinal common-sense inference. *Transactions of the Association for Computational Linguistics*, 5:379–395.

A Data Collection

Figure 12 shows that on certain examples human annotators vary in their truth judgements, with some sentences receiving a high score (i.e. "True") from certain annotators and a low score (i.e. "False") from others. Further inspection reveals that many of the highest-variance examples have one annotator who is an extreme outlier.

Figure 7 shows the MechanicalTurk annotator interface for collecting VQA and GQA annotations. The task was only available to annotators in the US with an approval rating $> 98\%$ and more than 500 recorded HITs. Instructions asked annotators to respond to the questions by using the sliding bar. They were provided with a comment box to use in case any issues arose.

Similarly, Figure 8 shows the interface for collecting text-only annotations. Here, the task was only shown to annotators from a list of reliable workers. Instructions asked annotators to rate how true a sentence was, and told that sentences may be true or false. They were instructed to use the "I don't know" checkbox in cases where they did not know a word in the statement.

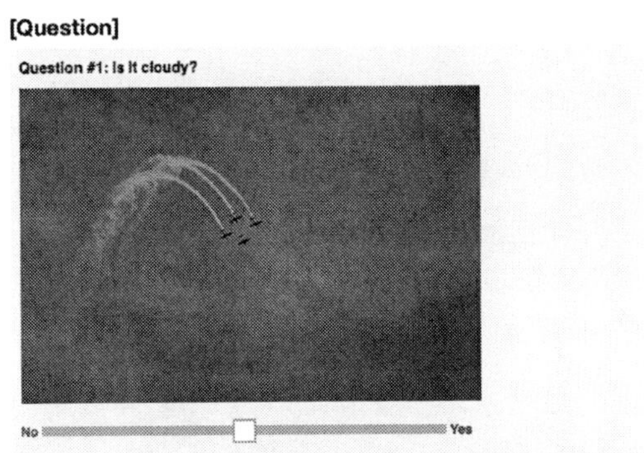

Figure 7: Mechanical Turk annotation template for visual annotations.

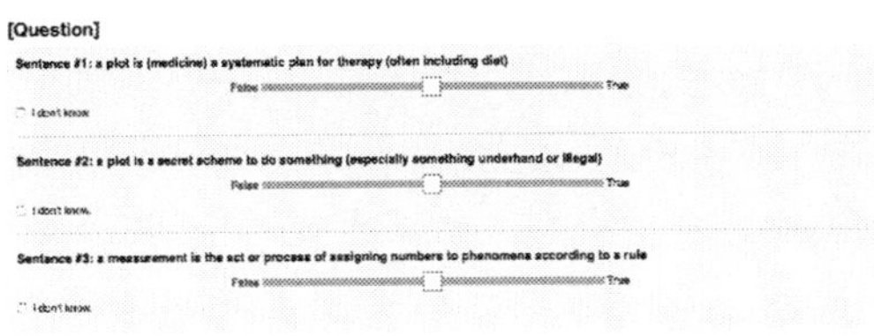

Figure 8: Mechanical Turk annotation template for text annotations.

B Plots

Figures 9 and 10 show human annotations plotted against model predictions for all of the predicates examined. In all cases, we see major divergences between human and model data, as quantified in Fig. 3. We also see that the standard error between annotators is fairly low. Furthermore, we see similar trends between descriptors across the two datasets, with "new" being skewed towards the higher end for both.

Figure 11 verifies that for the descriptors examined ("sunny" and "cloudy") the mean score obtained from annotators on Mechanical Turk and the mean score from the VQA development roughly correspond, justifying the use of the VQA development data in § 3. However, we do note some divergence between the two annotation formats, likely due to the forced choice presented to the original VQA annotators.

C Text Examples

Table 2 contains 28 example sentences from the validation set, with human classifications derived by majority voting over the annotators who did not use the "I don't know" box, as well as classifications obtained by the `[CLS]` model.

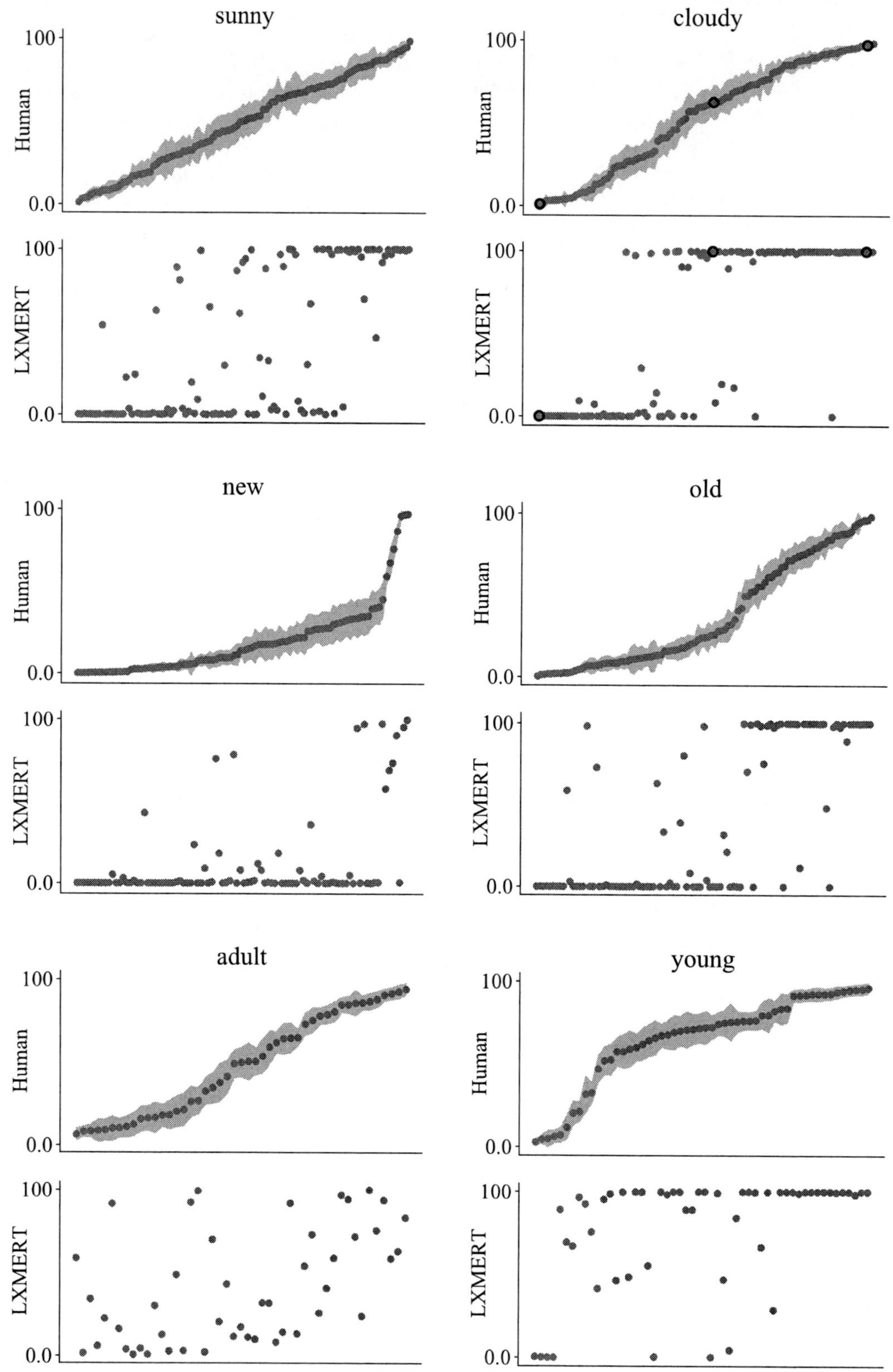

Figure 9: Human and model scores for questions containing vague terms from the GQA dataset.

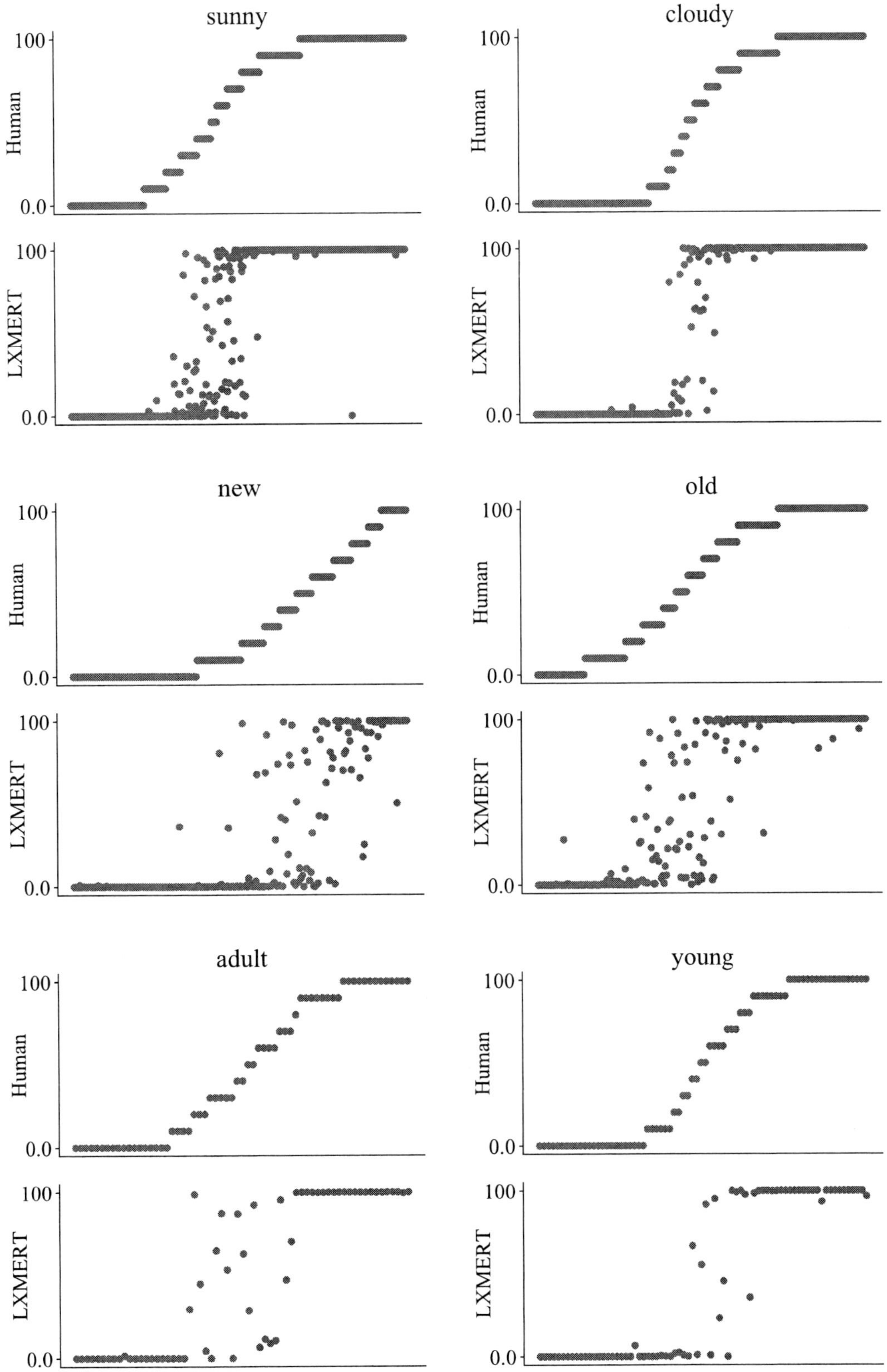

Figure 10: Average annotator scores and model scores for questions containing vague terms on the VQA dataset.

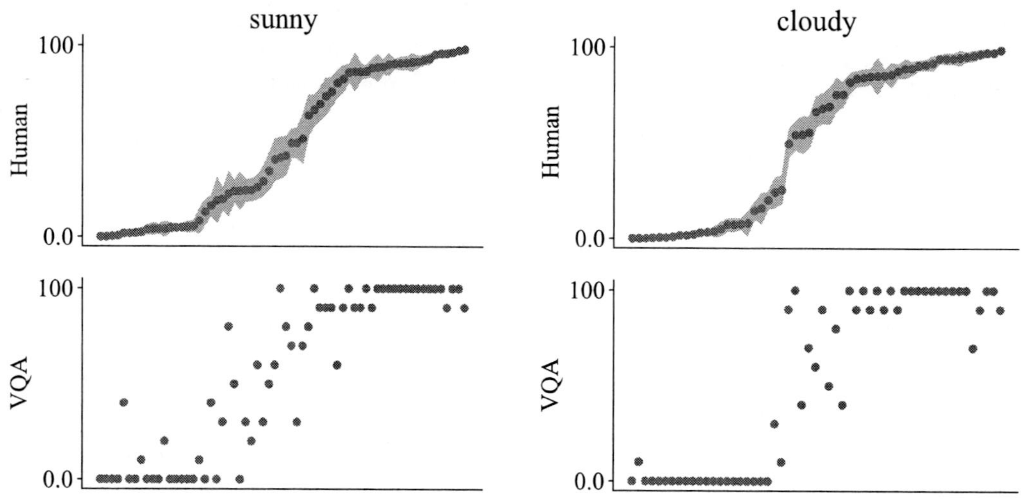

Figure 11: Manual verification of VQA plots shows that Mechanical Turker's judgments largely correspond to those present in the development set, with some divergence.

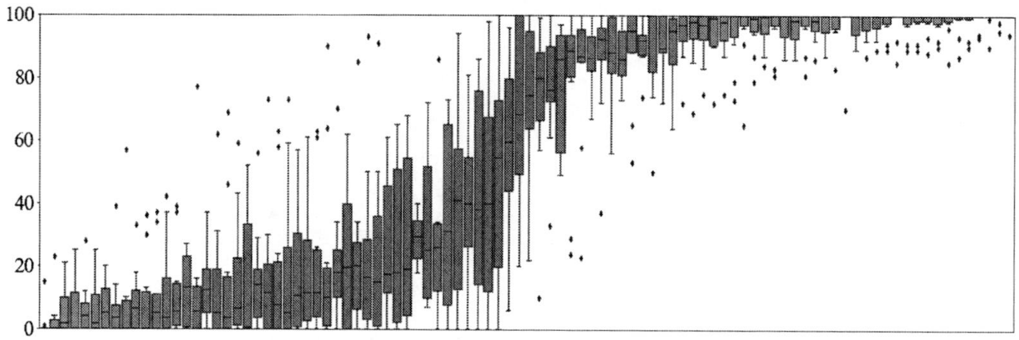

Figure 12: Human means and quartiles for examples ranked by average score

Sentence	Label	Human	XLNet	BERT	RoBERTa
a plot is (medicine) a systematic plan for therapy (often including diet)	F	21.90	1.00	0.22	0.49
a plot is a secret scheme to do something (especially something underhand or illegal)	T	95.60	1.00	0.38	0.31
a measurement is the act or process of assigning numbers to phenomena according to a rule	T	73.30	0.02	0.88	0.39
a measurement is a sudden event that imparts energy or excitement, usually with a dramatic impact	F	8.70	0.00	0.47	0.44
one is the product of two equal terms	F	21.33	0.04	0.72	0.49
one is the smallest whole number or a numeral representing this number	T	94.22	0.15	0.97	0.69
an exit is an opening that permits escape or release	T	97.90	0.94	0.93	0.79
an exit is a man-made object taken as a whole	F	7.30	0.00	0.01	0.09
a label is a brief description given for purposes of identification	T	95.20	1.00	0.62	0.33
a label is the act of having on your person as a covering or adornment	F	20.40	0.00	0.22	0.41
a ritual is the act of prolonging something	F	25.22	0.64	0.26	0.92
a ritual is any customary observance or practice	T	97.90	1.00	1.00	0.80
distance is faulty position	F	5.90	0.27	0.00	0.71
distance is the property created by the space between two objects or points	T	97.90	1.00	0.98	0.40
a shock is a lack of gratitude	F	7.67	0.00	0.29	0.27
a shock is the feeling of distress and disbelief that you have when something bad happens accidentally	T	96.10	0.53	0.03	0.74
a route is the frozen part of a body of water	F	7.30	0.00	0.88	0.73
a route is an established line of travel or access	T	97.90	0.79	0.89	1.00
a ban is a decree that prohibits something	T	97.70	1.00	0.75	0.83
a ban is a legal instrument authorizing someone to act as the grantor's agent	F	5.70	0.00	0.19	0.88
citizenship is the status of a citizen with rights and duties	T	96.20	1.00	0.91	1.00
citizenship is the state of having been made ready or prepared for use or action (especially military action)	F	12.56	0.00	0.07	1.00
an accent is distinctive manner of oral expression	T	90.30	0.97	0.58	0.53
an accent is (language) communication by word of mouth	F	47.56	0.03	0.08	0.22
journalism is newspapers and magazines collectively	T	81.89	0.02	0.96	0.32
journalism is an artifact made of hard brittle material produced from nonmetallic minerals by firing at high temperatures	F	1.60	0.00	0.00	0.88
atmosphere is a particular environment or surrounding influence	T	87.20	1.00	0.52	0.72
atmosphere is any attribute or immaterial possession that is inherited from ancestors	F	12.56	0.00	0.00	0.31

Table 2: Sentences, labels, human means and model logits for 28 sample validation examples.

A Mention-Based System for Revision Requirements Detection

Ahmed Ruby[1], Christian Hardmeier[1,2] and Sara Stymne[1]
[1]Uppsala University, Department of Linguistics and Philology
[2]IT University of Copenhagen, Department of Computer Science
firstName.lastName@lingfil.uu.se

Abstract

Exploring aspects of sentential meaning that are implicit or underspecified in context is important for sentence understanding. In this paper, we propose a novel architecture based on mentions for revision requirements detection. The goal is to improve understandability, addressing some types of revisions, especially for the Replaced Pronoun type. We show that our mention-based system can predict replaced pronouns well on the mention-level. However, our combined sentence-level system does not improve on the sentence-level BERT baseline. We also present additional contrastive systems, and show results for each type of edit.

1 Introduction

The Revision Requirements task aims to recognize whether or not a sentence requires revision. Revision Requirements prediction not only acts as a standalone tool for grammar correction but also has potential applications in natural language processing (NLP) such as ambiguity detection, machine translation refinement, sentence understanding, knowledge base construction, etc.

The shared task on implicit and underspecified language (Roth and Anthonio, 2021)[1] aims to provide a binary classification for revision requirements to make a prediction of whether sentences in instructional texts require revision to improve understandability. Since instructional texts must be clear enough so that readers and machines can actually achieve the goal described by the instructions, this task focuses on modeling implicit elements that make the sentence more precise and clear. The dataset used in this shared task consists of instances from wikiHowToImprove, a collection of instructional texts, which has recently been introduced by Anthonio et al. (2020). It contains six types of edits:

- Replacements of pronouns with more precise noun phrases (REPLACED_PRONOUN)
- Replacements of 'do' as a full verb with more precise verbs (REPLACED_DO)
- Insertions of optional verbal phrase complements (ADDED_ARG)
- Insertions of adverbial and adjectival modifiers (ADDED_MOD)
- Insertions of quantifiers (ADDED_QUANT)
- Insertions of modal verbs (ADDED_MOD)

The shared task submission requires only a binary distinction between sentences that require revision and sentences that do not.

A good instructional text consists of specific instructions to accomplish the goal described and tends to avoid vague, generic and generalizing sentences. Whilst checking the edit types in the revised version, especially "Replacements of pronouns with more precise noun phrases", we observed that replacements occur primarily with generic pronouns that do not refer to a specific individual or set of individuals, but to a type or class of individuals. Table 1 shows examples with generic pronouns that require revision.

For this reason, we believe and show that identifying generic pronouns and noun phrases helps to predict whether a sentence requires revision for the REVISED_PRONOUN class. For instance, if the pronoun has a co-reference in the sentence, it should not be replaced with a noun phrase. As a result, our proposed classification model for the task of Revision Requirements Detection is based on extracting mention embeddings for each sentence

[1]https://unimplicit.github.io

Proceedings of the 1st Workshop on Understanding Implicit and Underspecified Language (UnImplicit 2021), pages 58–63
Bangkok, Thailand (online), August 5, 2021.

Generic pronouns
They make a sound that dogs can hear, but humans can't.
Double check that **it** will be level using a level.
Your parents may not like any of **them**.
Burn **it** to a CD.
Let **us** have bad days.
You cannot be offside directly from a corner-kick.

Table 1: Examples with generic pronouns that require revision.

using a neural coreference resolution system[2] and feed them into a classification layer (multi-layer perceptron) to predict for each individual mention whether or not it requires revision.

Our approach uses the Neuralcoref resolution system to get mention embeddings for the target sentence. In addition we also extract embeddings for each mention based on BERT (Devlin et al., 2019) for each mention. In this approach, we predicted revisions at the mention level. Labels for the mentions were created based on a comparison between the original sentence, and the revised sentence, where we checked if any word had been changed, added or removed from each mention. For sentences for which we could not extract any mentions, we used a basic sentence-level Bert-based system, since the BERT model achieved the highest F1-score in previous work (Bhat et al., 2020).

In summary, we show that our mention-based system works well for replaced pronouns, but as expected, it is not successful for the other classes, which it does not target. Our final system is overall slightly worse than our sentence-based system based on BERT. At the mention-level our system performs well for replaced pronouns.

2 Related Work

There has been a lot of work on revisions to improve understandability, Tan and Lee (2014) conducted research on revisions in academic writing, using a qualitative approach to distinguish between strong and weak sentences, by analyzing the differences in the original and revised sentences.

Afrin and Litman (2018) introduced a classification model based on Random Forest (RF) for revisions in argumentative essays from ArgRewrite (Zhang et al., 2017) to examine whether we can predict improvement for non-expert and predict if the revised sentence is better than the original.

Anthonio et al. (2020) worked with edits in instructional texts and applied a supervised learning approach to distinguish older and newer versions of a sentence between wikiHow and Wikipedia.

Recent work by Bhat et al. (2020) presents an automatic classification of revision requirements in wikiHow, used the BERT model to achieve the highest F1-score, reporting 68.42% predicting revision requirements, outperforming the Naive Bayes and BiLSTM models by 4.39 and 7.67 percentage points, respectively. We consider the BERT Model as a strong baseline for our experiments from Bhat et al. (2020).

[2]https://github.com/huggingface/neuralcoref

Dataset	Req_Revision	N. of sentences
Training set	19599	39187
Development set	1632	3264
Test set		3458

Table 2: Statistics of the dataset.

3 Dataset

We used the dataset provided by the organizers of the shared task on revision requirements prediction. This dataset contains instances that were extracted from the revision histories of www.wikiHow.com articles. These how-to articles cover many fields such as Arts and Entertainment, Computers and Electronics, Health, along with their revision history. The revisions and classes were extracted automatically from the training data. The development and test data was verified by human annotators (see Roth and Anthonio, 2021, for details).

There are two subsets:

- Sentences extracted from the revision history, which later received edits which made the sentence more precise. These are labelled REQ_REVISION.
- Sentences that remained unchanged over multiple revisions of the article. These are labelled KEEP_UNREVIS.

The dataset includes training, development and test sets. However, the type of edit in case of a revision and the revised version of the target sentence, are available only for the training set. We therefore used k-fold cross-validation to randomly partition the training set into 5 equal-sized subsamples for training and development, for which we needed access to the revised sentences. Table 2 shows how the dataset is balanced.[3]

[3]The test set is not released to participants, so we cannot report all test set statistics.

Dataset	Req_Revision	N. of mentions
Training set	2901	16976
Development set	749	4339
Test set		2368

Table 3: Statistics of the mentions in the dataset.

We used SpaCy's (Honnibal et al., 2020) tokenizer to tokenize the target sentences and the context since the current dataset does not include the tokenized version of the context.

4 Mention Extraction

Based on our observation that generic noun phrases often lead to revision, we hypothesize that extracting mentions based on a coreference resolution system might help in identifying such instances. We believe that this architecture might be especially useful for replacements of pronouns with more specific noun phrases and the insertion of logical quantifiers. We use Huggingface's NeuralCoref system, which is based on spaCy library, to extract mentions from our dataset.[4] Table 3 shows statistics of the mentions in the dataset.

In order to create labels for mentions, we extracted the class of each token for the input target sentence by comparing the target with the revised sentences. We use the Python *difflib* library to align the original and revised sentence. We can then assign a positive label if any word in a mention was removed, changed or inserted and a negative label otherwise.

5 Mention Embeddings

Since we need to capture the coreference information within the span of mentions in the embeddings, we produced two versions of the mention embeddings, one with dimension 650 using Neuralcoref resolution system and a second of dimension 768 using BERT-as-service.

5.1 Mention NeuralCoref Embeddings

We use Huggingface's NeuralCoref system as well to get embeddings for mentions, which is based on SpaCy's model en_core_web_lg. All embeddings are extracted for all mentions found in the target sentence.

5.2 Mention BERT Embeddings

We use bert-as-service,[5] uncased model, to generate the BERT embeddings, with our own per-mention reduction, which takes the vectors for each word and does the mean reduction for these vectors which were extracted corresponding to the span of the mention.

5.3 Concatenating the BERT and NeuralCoref embeddings

We also try using the combination of both embeddings. Therefore, we concatenated the BERT embeddings and neuralcoref vectors. the dimensions of the concatenated output vector are 1418.

6 Experimental and Model Design

In this section, we present initial exploratory experiments and the process behind building a model that addresses the two obstacles to combine the predictions of the mention-level system into the sentence-level BERT backup system.

6.1 Mention-Level System

For the mention-level, we use a feed-forward neural network with the different types of mention embedding as input to classify whether the mention requires revision or not.

We train a Multi Layer Perceptron (MLP) using mention embeddings as input, with using a single hidden layer consisting of 100 hidden units and a rectified linear (ReLU) activation function, and the final linear layer with a sigmoid function to make predictions. Since the mention dataset is not balanced, the classifier sees many more negative than positive examples. We try to counteract this by giving higher weight to the positive examples using class weights. For experiments on the training data, where we use cross-validation, the weights for the negative and positive classes, were set to 0.854 and 0.146 respectively while the weights for the full training data for the negative and positive classes, were set to 0.840 and 0.160 respectively.

We run 3 experiments with different inputs, mention NeuralCoref embeddings (M), mention BERT Embeddings (MB) and mention BERT and neuralcoref embeddings concatenated (M+MB).

All models are trained for 100 epochs and with a learning rate of 0.01, and training examples are presented in random order. For experiments on the

[4]https://github.com/huggingface/neuralcoref.

[5]https://github.com/hanxiao/bert-as-service

training data, where we use cross-validation, we report the average scores across the five folds.

6.2 Sentence-Level System

For the sentence-level system, we use BERT-Base (Devlin et al., 2019), uncased model (12 transformer blocks, 768 hidden size, 12 attention heads and 110M parameters) fine-tuned with an additional output layer on top of BERT's final representation. We use the Huggingface Transformers library with TensorFlow and load a pre-trained BERT from the Transformers library. We train this model for 2 epochs with a learning rate of $3 \cdot 10^{-5}$ and batch size 32.

The mention-level system does not have extracted mentions for all sentences, and therefore does not provide predictions for all sentences. In our combined system we use the predictions from the mention-level system as our primary predictions; if there is a positive prediction for any mention in a sentence, that sentence is labelled as positive. Sentences where all mentions are labelled negative receive a negative label. For sentences without extracted mentions, we use the predictions by the sentence-level BERT-based system.

As a further point of comparison we also provide an oracle combination of the two systems. In the oracle we only use the predictions from the mention-based systems for those sentences where there is at least one mention which requires an edit, i.e. which has a positive gold label. The purpose of this oracle is to give an idea of how well our mention-based system performs on mentions where we know an edit is required. For all other sentences, the oracle uses the prediction from the sentence-level BERT-based system.

7 Results and Analysis

This section presents an overview of our experiments and findings. We compare our results with the BERT model baseline that set the previous state-of-the-art performance. We also present results on specific types of revisions since our approach was targeted mainly at the "replaced pronoun" class. We perform the majority of our analysis on training set, presented in Tables 4–7, which is the only data set which contains class labels and revised sentences. Precision, recall, and F_1-score is shown for requiring revision as the positive class.

The most successful model on mention-level is the system with only mention Bert embeddings

Model	Precision	Recall	F_1-score	Acc
M	0.0292	0.2000	0.0510	0.7123
MB	0.2646	0.6783	0.3799	0.6772
M+MB	0.2575	0.7273	0.3797	0.6523

Table 4: Results of our models on mention-level.

Types of revision	MB
ADDED_ARG	0.4208
ADDED_MOD	0.0578
ADDED_MODAL	0.1500
ADDED_QUANT	0.1768
REPLACED_DO	0.6492
REPLACED_PRONOUN	0.9064

Table 5: Recall for each type of edits on the mention-level

(MB), as shown in Table 4. The system using mention Neural Coref embeddings is not successful and always predicts a single class; in all folds but one it predicts the negative class only. The difference between using only BERT embeddings and combining the two embedding types is small.

Table 5 shows the results for each type of edit, for the best mention-level system, with BERT embeddings. Here we can only show recall, since our system does not predict the individual classes. The results confirm that our system is useful for detecting the pronoun replacement class as revision requirements, but that it gives poor results for the other classes, especially for added modifiers, modals, and quantifiers.

Table 6 shows the results of our models on the sentence-level. Overall it is clear that the sentence-level BERT-based system is better than the mention-based combinations, shown in the middle, especially with respect to recall. The M+BERT system has the lowest recall. The bottom row shows the oracle scores for the MB+BERT system, which gives slightly better results than the BERT baseline on all metrics, which indicates that the decisions made by the mention-based system are good with respect to sentences where an extracted mention requires revision. The oracle is considerably better than the standard combination, especially for recall, since the mention-based system does not really have a chance to predict anything useful for sentences where the edit does not occur in one of our extracted mentions.

Table 7 shows recall for each type of edit on the sentence-level. The sentence-level BERT-based system still achieves the highest scores for all classes compared to the standard combination. The oracle combination shows an improvement for the

Model	Precision	Recall	F_1-score	Acc
BERT	0.6628	0.5997	0.6275	0.6460
M+BERT	0.6459	0.3816	0.4742	0.5847
MB+BERT	0.6470	0.4906	0.5567	0.6107
M+MB+BERT	0.6455	0.4989	0.5617	0.6118
MB+BERT oracle	0.6654	0.6064	0.6324	0.6493

Table 6: Results for predicting revision requirements at the sentence-level. The top row is the BERT sentence-level baseline, the middle rows shows the combined system, and the bottom row the oracle combination for MB embeddings.

Types of revision	BERT	MB+BERT	MB+BERT oracle
ADDED_ARG	0.7506	0.6369	0.7495
ADDED_MOD	0.4731	0.4121	0.4719
ADDED_MODAL	0.6573	0.5505	0.6563
ADDED_QUANT	0.4236	0.3588	0.4244
REPLACED_DO	0.7848	0.6737	0.7828
REPLACED_PRONOUN	0.8229	0.5856	0.8586

Table 7: Recall for each type of edit on the Sentence-level

Model	Precision	Recall	F_1-score	Acc
BERT	0.7044	0.6146	0.6564	0.6783
M	0.6590	0.5472	0.5979	0.6320
MB	0.6891	0.4522	0.5461	0.6241
M+MB	0.6831	0.4914	0.5716	0.6317

Table 8: Sentence-level results on the development set.

replaced pronoun class compared to the BERT baseline. For the other classes the difference to the baseline is small for the oracle, with only slightly lower results, which indicates that the mention-based system hardly ever predicts an edit for the other classes, and the few times it does so, it is mainly erroneous.

Table 8 shows the results on the provided development sets. These results are generated by using only the standard combination since we do not have gold labels for the mentions, since no revised sentences were provided for the development set. The BERT model achieves the highest F_1-score, outperforming the M, MB and M+MB by 4.63, 5.42 and 4.66 percentage points, while the M outperforms the MB and M+MB models by 9.50 and 5.58 percentage points in recall since the M system only predicts a single class.

We submitted the combination system based on MB embeddings to the shared task.[6] For our submitted predictions on the test, which was evaluated by the organizers in terms of accuracy, measured as the ratio of correct predictions over all data instances (Roth and Anthonio, 2021), we achieved 66.3% accuracy for the mention-based system, which is higher than the logistic regression baseline provided by the organizers. Our sentence-level BERT-based system achieved 68.6% accuracy on the test set.

[6]Our original submission had a bug, leading to low scores. We thus report results for our updated submission, without this bug, which is also reported in Roth and Anthonio (2021).

8 Conclusions and Future Work

In this paper, we show that identifying generic mentions can improve the performance of the replaced pronoun type. We introduced a mention-based system for predicting whether a sentence requires revision. Investigating methods for combining a general classifier such as BERT, with systems that target specific edits, such as our mention-based system, would be an interesting avenue for future work. As a next step, we plan to apply this idea to other languages and address other types of revisions.

Acknowledgements

Christian Hardmeier was supported by the Swedish Research Council under grant 2017-930.

References

Tazin Afrin and Diane Litman. 2018. Annotation and classification of sentence-level revision improvement. In *Proceedings of the Thirteenth Workshop on Innovative Use of NLP for Building Educational Applications*, pages 240–246, New Orleans, Louisiana. Association for Computational Linguistics.

Talita Anthonio, Irshad Bhat, and Michael Roth. 2020. wikiHowToImprove: A resource and analyses on edits in instructional texts. In *Proceedings of the 12th Language Resources and Evaluation Conference*, pages 5721–5729, Marseille, France. European Language Resources Association.

Irshad Bhat, Talita Anthonio, and Michael Roth. 2020. Towards modeling revision requirements in wikiHow instructions. In *Proceedings of the 2020 Conference on Empirical Methods in Natural Language Processing (EMNLP)*, pages 8407–8414, Online. Association for Computational Linguistics.

Jacob Devlin, Ming-Wei Chang, Kenton Lee, and Kristina Toutanova. 2019. BERT: Pre-training of deep bidirectional transformers for language understanding. In *Proceedings of the 2019 Conference of the North American Chapter of the Association for Computational Linguistics: Human Language Technologies, Volume 1 (Long and Short Papers)*, pages 4171–4186, Minneapolis, Minnesota. Association for Computational Linguistics.

Matthew Honnibal, Ines Montani, Sofie Van Landeghem, and Adriane Boyd. 2020. spaCy: Industrial-strength Natural Language Processing in Python.

Michael Roth and Talita Anthonio. 2021. Unimplicit shared task report: Detecting clarification requirements in instructional text. In *Proceedings of the First Workshop on Understanding Implicit and Underspecified Language*.

Chenhao Tan and Lillian Lee. 2014. A corpus of sentence-level revisions in academic writing: A step towards understanding statement strength in communication. In *Proceedings of the 52nd Annual Meeting of the Association for Computational Linguistics (Volume 2: Short Papers)*, pages 403–408, Baltimore, Maryland. Association for Computational Linguistics.

Fan Zhang, Homa B. Hashemi, Rebecca Hwa, and Diane Litman. 2017. A corpus of annotated revisions for studying argumentative writing. In *Proceedings of the 55th Annual Meeting of the Association for Computational Linguistics (Volume 1: Long Papers)*, pages 1568–1578, Vancouver, Canada. Association for Computational Linguistics.

TTCB System Description to a Shared Task on Implicit and Underspecified Language 2021

Peratham Wiriyathammabhum
peratham.bkk@gmail.com

Abstract

In this report, we describe our Transformers for text classification baseline (TTCB) submissions to a shared task on implicit and underspecified language 2021. We cast the task of predicting revision requirements in collaboratively edited instructions as text classification. We considered Transformer-based models which are the current state-of-the-art methods for text classification. We explored different training schemes, loss functions, and data augmentations. Our best result of *68.45%* test accuracy (*68.84%* validation accuracy), however, consists of an XLNet model with a linear annealing scheduler and a cross-entropy loss. We do not observe any significant gain on any validation metric based on our various design choices except the MiniLM which has a higher validation F1 score and is faster to train by a half but also a lower validation accuracy score.

1 Introduction

A shared task on implicit and underspecified language 2021 is the first installment of predicting revision requirements in collaboratively edited instructions (Bhat et al., 2020) based on the wikiHowToImprove dataset (Anthonio et al., 2020). The dataset consists of sentences and their revisions if any. There are *5* rule-based revision types which are pronoun replacement, 'do' verb replacement, verbal phrase compliment insertion, adverbial and adjectival modifier insertion, and logical quantifier or modal verb insertion. The task is to determine whether a given sentence with its corresponding context paragraph needs any revision based on the aforementioned revision types.

Previous work (Bhat et al., 2020) compares BERT (Devlin et al., 2019) and BiLSTM on the full wikiHowToImprove dataset which has *2.7* millions sentences. The previous experiment integrates *4.25* millions of unrevised sentences from wikiHow to further balance the training set. Their results suggest BERT over BiLSTM. Our systems build upon this finding and further explore Transformer-based models.

Table 1: Example instances from the wikiHowToImprove dataset. The first sentence does not require any revision. The second sentence needs a revision by replacing the pronoun 'They' with the word 'Meeting' to provide more clarity.

Sentence	Label
Do not pour the petals in the perfume on storing .	KEEP_UNREVIS
They also give managers the opportunity to tell everyone the same thing at once , which can cut down on gossip .	REQ_REVISION

The codes for our systems are open-sourced and available at our GitHub repository[1].

2 Models

2.1 XLNet

XLNet (Yang et al., 2019) is the current state-of-the-art for text classification on various benchmarks such as DBpedia, AG, Amazon-2, and Amazon-5. XLNet is an autoregressive Transformer language model which further explores longer context modeling to capture long-term dependencies between words. We consider the HuggingFace Transformer library (Wolf et al., 2020) for our experiments on XLNet.

2.2 Siamese training

Siamese model training (Bromley et al., 1993) is an off-the-shelf neural-networks training paradigm that learns similarity embedding for verification by using two identical neural networks to extract

[1] https://github.com/perathambkk/unimplicit_shared_task_acl_2021

Proceedings of the 1st Workshop on Understanding Implicit and Underspecified Language (UnImplicit 2021), pages 64–70
Bangkok, Thailand (online), August 5, 2021.

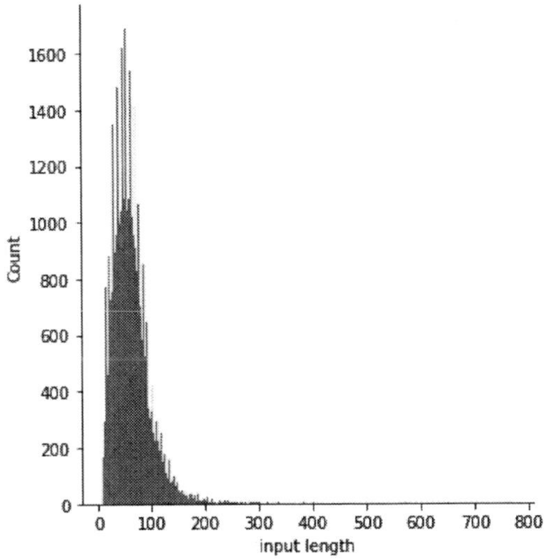

Figure 1: **The distribution of the input length derived from the shared task training set.**

feature vectors for a threshold-based input pair comparison. The model is learned from the signal whether an input pair is similar or dissimilar. This approach has been shown in various settings to produce a good vector embedding space. We consider the sentence-Transformers library (Reimers and Gurevych, 2019) for our experiments on Siamese training.

3 Experimental Setup

Our input is a simple concatenation of a sentence and its context paragraph. We tried different context lengths and found that *128* yields the best result. From Figure 1, the mean input length is only *62.58* with the standard deviation of *36.00*. This is from the shared task dataset which is the subset of the original wikiHowToImprove dataset and has *45,909* sentences in total (*39,187* sentences in the training set.). The statistics suggest setting the context length less than *200* to be cost-effective and there are only *1,632* training instances (around *4%*) having their input lengths longer than *128* with the maximum length of *770*.

All of our experiments were done in the Google Colab setting. We used only base models for all Transformers. We used the batch size of *8* and the learning rate of *1e-5* for all experiments. We considered linear annealing scheduler since other schedulers, such as ReduceLR scheduler, cosine annealing scheduler, or cosine annealing scheduler with restart, do not provide any significantly different results. Also, adding a warm-up step does not make any difference too. We trained the model for

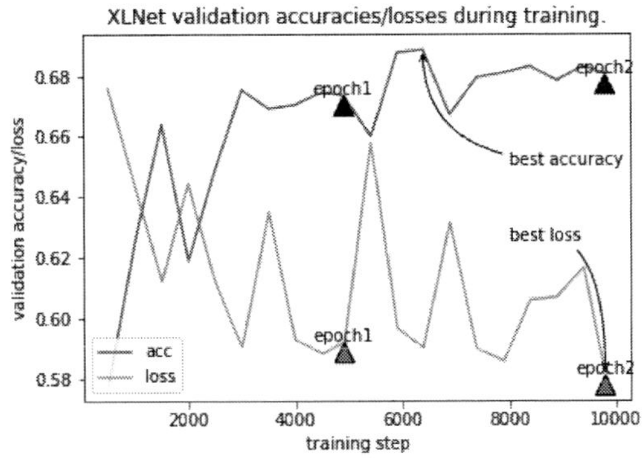

Figure 2: **Validation accuracies and losses during training of the XLNet model.**

Table 2: Development accuracies of text classification Transformer models. Majority means always predicting using the majority class label which is either always positive or negative in this balanced development set.

Model	Dev Accuracy
Majority	50.00
OpenGPT-2	65.50
XLNet	**68.84**
Bigbird	68.69

4 epochs (following the standard fine-tuning procedure in the original BERT paper (Devlin et al., 2019) which recommends *2-4* epochs.) and sample a model state at every *500* training steps for evaluation on the development set. Most of the best models are from the second epoch. This step helps to save the best model parameter state which could be empirically up to *1%* better in development accuracy than only collecting the model state at the end of each training epoch as depicted in Figure 2 for XLNet.

3.1 Text Classification

We compare XLNet with OpenGPT-2 (Radford et al., 2019) and Bigbird (Zaheer et al., 2020) for text sequence classification in Table 2. OpenGPT-2 is an unsupervised multitask language model. Bigbird is a recent state-of-the-art text classification model on some benchmarks, such as arXiv (He et al., 2019), Patents (Lee and Hsiang, 2020), or Hyperpartisan (Kiesel et al., 2019). Bigbird utilizes better computation methods to efficiently model longer sequence lengths than XLNet. The results suggest that modeling longer sequence length than a sentence helps as seen in XLNet and Bigbird, however, Bigbird is only comparable to XLNet in terms of accuracy.

Table 3: Development accuracies of different loss functions on the XLNet model.

Loss Function	Dev Accuracy
binary cross-entropy (BCE)	**68.84**
label smoothed BCE	68.78
cost-sensitive BCE	68.81
cost-sensitive multiclass CE	67.80

Table 4: Development accuracies of data augmented Bigbird.

Augmentation	Dev Accuracy
Bigbird	**68.69**
+ negative class augmentation	64.74
+ cost-sensitive BCE	68.47

3.2 Loss Functions

Label smoothing (Szegedy et al., 2016) is a design choice in loss function which helps improve the model performance in many tasks by smoothing the cross-entropy label loss from *0/1* to α/K for other classes and $(1-\alpha)$ for the target class using an arbitrary hyperparameter α. We used the α value of *0.1*.

Previous work (Bhat et al., 2020) also emphasizes the class-imbalance issue in this task. Therefore, we tried cost-sensitive cross-entropy loss to weigh more on the positive class (revision needed) which suppose to have more information. We weighted the positive class by *0.6* and the negative class by *0.4*. We also tried cost-sensitive multiclass cross-entropy loss where we train on revision types as the label set and convert them to *0/1* for prediction with the hope that the model might better learn the structure in the data. We weighted each class by the inverse of its number of instances.

The results in Table 3 suggest that there might not be any significant class-imbalance issue that can be alleviated via various cost function design choices since the development accuracies are very much the same. The exception is the multiclass setting where we conjecture that that revision types might make the training task harder instead.

3.3 Data Augmentation

The shared task data provide the revisions when the labels are positive (revision needed) so we tried to generate more data from these. We assumed the revised sentences provide more signals of no revision required. Therefore, we simply put the negative label on those sentences. We hoped that these data instances will provide more useful learning signals when added to the training set as more informative negative instances. Our reason is it should be more certain that most revised sentences should not require revisions, at least from the revised type. From Table 4, we chose Bigbird since it is more computationally efficient. However, adding more data does not improve the performance. Instead, the performance decreases to *64.74%* accuracy. Still, adding cost-sensitive binary cross-entropy can bring the accuracy back to be comparable to a vanilla Bigbird. This indicates that cost-sensitive loss may be helpful if we were to perform data augmentation. The cost-sensitive binary cross-entropy loss function adds a scalar weighting w to the cross-entropy loss term for each class.

Table 5: Development accuracies and F1 scores on CrossEncoder or BinaryEncoder for text classification.

Model	Dev Accuracy	F1 Score
XLNet	**68.84**	70.08
MiniLM-L-12	68.44	71.72
Siamese-BERT	63.57	69.77

$$loss(x, class) = w[class] \cdot (-x[class] + \log\left(\textstyle\sum_j (exp(x[j]))\right) \quad (1)$$

Since the revision types are based on syntax, we also tried to add more syntactic information to the models. Our preliminary attempt is to add part-of-speech tags and dependency trees (tagged using spaCy (Honnibal et al., 2020)) as additional context inputs by concatenation to existing sentence and context inputs. However, they do not provide any useful learning signals as also observed from recent attempts to learn syntactic Transformers. We also tried to learn solely from part-of-speech tags and dependency trees inputs and they provide very low accuracies similar to random. Many recent studies (Clark et al., 2019; Hewitt and Manning, 2019; Rogers et al., 2020) also show that BERT learns some syntactic information during its pretraining steps. However, there are still some works (Sundararaman et al., 2019; Wang et al., 2020a) showing that explicitly adding syntactic information may still improve BERT or Transformer performance.

3.4 Siamese Training

To begin with, the sentence-Transformers library (Reimers and Gurevych, 2019) supports both CrossEncoder (the same architecture for text classification) and BiEncoder (Siamese training). We tried their CrossEncoder model with MiniLM-L-12 model (Wang et al., 2020b) pretrained on ms-marco (Nguyen et al., 2016) for passage reranking

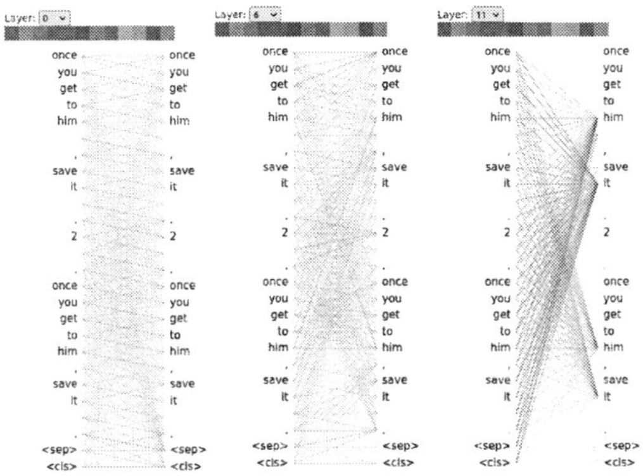

Figure 3: **BertViz XLNet attention-head visualization from the first attention head of layers $\{1, 7, 12\}$ for a revision-required sentence, 'Once you get to him, save it.'**

(slightly after the competition). The results in Table 5 indicate a lower development accuracy for MiniLM-L-12 but a comparable F1 score. The advantage of MiniLM-L-12 is its training cost is less than half of the XLNet model. We observed the speed-up on an NVIDIA-K80, an NVIDIA-P100, and an NVIDIA-T4 GPU from Google's Colab in our experiments. MiniLM is more lightweight and may be suitable for faster research cycles in general. Next, we depict our results on vanilla Siamese-BERT. We speculate that sentence embedding models have effortlessly good F1 scores because of their higher recall based on the nature of embedding vector spaces.

3.5 Visualizing XLNet

We consider BertViz (Vig, 2019) to explain the XLNet model via attention visualization. Figure 3 shows the attention weights from layers $\{1, 7, 12\}$ for a revision-required input sentence from the development set, 'Once you get to him, save it.' The visualization suggests that early layers learn simple and local patterns while middle layers learn longer dependencies and the top layers learn revision patterns. This is from the rightmost plot which shows large weights on the terms, 'him' and 'it', which probably require revisions.

Figure 4 shows another example from a no-revision-required input sentence from the development set, 'It's at the bottom of the page.' The early and middle layers exhibit similar patterns as the previous example which are local or longer dependencies. However, the top layers show even weighting for each word in the input sentence which instead does not indicate any revision signal. From the model views which show all attention heads in all

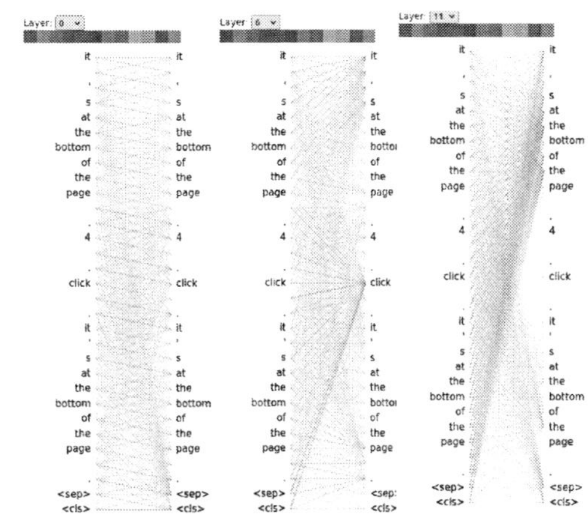

Figure 4: **BertViz XLNet attention-head visualization from the first attention head of layers $\{1, 7, 12\}$ for a no-revision-required sentence, 'It's at the bottom of the page.'**

layers in Figure 5 and Figure 6, the visualizations suggest that different attention heads from the same layer exhibit similar patterns.

4 Conclusion

This report describes our baseline systems for a shared task on implicit and underspecified language 2021, predicting revision requirements in wikiHow. Our best result is from the XLNet model with a linear annealing scheduler and a cross-entropy loss. We do not observe any significant gain on any validation metric based on our various design choices. The cost-sensitive loss might help only when performing data augmentation. MiniLM is comparable to XLNet but at a half computation cost. We summarize the results as finetuning Transformer-based language models for text classification only provides incremental improvements even though better language models consistently lead to better results. Also, the accuracies at most $\sim 70\%$ are not very practical. This suggests a big challenge for the language models in the context of implicit and underspecified language. We release our training code as an unofficial baseline for the challenge.

There are many possible future directions. First, we have not considered any advanced loss functions, such as Triplet loss (Weinberger et al., 2005; Hoffer and Ailon, 2015), for our Siamese training experiments. Second, recent work on predicting revisions in wikiHow (Debnath and Roth, 2021) depicts a promising integration of syntactic preprocessing and sentence embedding training. Nevertheless, more data analysis is needed to pinpoint what a particular model should learn.

Figure 5: **BertViz XLNet model-view shows all attention heads from all layers for a revision-required sentence, 'Once you get to him, save it.' Each row corresponds to a layer and each column corresponds to an attention head.**

Figure 6: **BertViz XLNet model-view shows all attention heads from all layers for no-revision-required sentence, 'It's at the bottom of the page.' Each row corresponds to a layer and each column corresponds to an attention head.**

Acknowledgments

We would like to thank anonymous reviewers for their constructive feedback.

References

Talita Anthonio, Irshad Bhat, and Michael Roth. 2020. wikiHowToImprove: A resource and analyses on edits in instructional texts. In *Proceedings of the 12th Language Resources and Evaluation Conference*, pages 5721–5729, Marseille, France. European Language Resources Association.

Irshad Bhat, Talita Anthonio, and Michael Roth. 2020. Towards modeling revision requirements in wikiHow instructions. In *Proceedings of the 2020 Conference on Empirical Methods in Natural Language Processing (EMNLP)*, pages 8407–8414, Online. Association for Computational Linguistics.

Jane Bromley, Isabelle Guyon, Yann LeCun, Eduard Säckinger, and Roopak Shah. 1993. Signature verification using a" siamese" time delay neural network. *Advances in neural information processing systems*, 6:737–744.

Kevin Clark, Urvashi Khandelwal, Omer Levy, and Christopher D Manning. 2019. What does bert look at? an analysis of bert's attention. In *Proceedings of the 2019 ACL Workshop BlackboxNLP: Analyzing and Interpreting Neural Networks for NLP*, pages 276–286.

Alok Debnath and Michael Roth. 2021. A computational analysis of vagueness in revisions of instructional texts. In *Proceedings of the 16th Conference of the European Chapter of the Association for Computational Linguistics: Student Research Workshop*, pages 30–35.

Jacob Devlin, Ming-Wei Chang, Kenton Lee, and Kristina Toutanova. 2019. Bert: Pre-training of deep bidirectional transformers for language understanding. In *Proceedings of the 2019 Conference of the North American Chapter of the Association for Computational Linguistics: Human Language Technologies, Volume 1 (Long and Short Papers)*, pages 4171–4186.

Jun He, Liqun Wang, Liu Liu, Jiao Feng, and Hao Wu. 2019. Long document classification from local word glimpses via recurrent attention learning. *IEEE Access*, 7:40707–40718.

John Hewitt and Christopher D Manning. 2019. A structural probe for finding syntax in word representations. In *Proceedings of the 2019 Conference of the North American Chapter of the Association for Computational Linguistics: Human Language Technologies, Volume 1 (Long and Short Papers)*, pages 4129–4138.

Elad Hoffer and Nir Ailon. 2015. Deep metric learning using triplet network. In *International workshop on similarity-based pattern recognition*, pages 84–92. Springer.

Matthew Honnibal, Ines Montani, Sofie Van Landeghem, and Adriane Boyd. 2020. spaCy: Industrial-strength Natural Language Processing in Python.

Johannes Kiesel, Maria Mestre, Rishabh Shukla, Emmanuel Vincent, Payam Adineh, David Corney, Benno Stein, and Martin Potthast. 2019. Semeval-2019 task 4: Hyperpartisan news detection. In *Proceedings of the 13th International Workshop on Semantic Evaluation*, pages 829–839.

Jieh-Sheng Lee and Jieh Hsiang. 2020. Patent classification by fine-tuning bert language model. *World Patent Information*, 61:101965.

Tri Nguyen, Mir Rosenberg, Xia Song, Jianfeng Gao, Saurabh Tiwary, Rangan Majumder, and Li Deng. 2016. Ms marco: A human generated machine reading comprehension dataset. In *CoCo@ NIPS*.

Alec Radford, Jeffrey Wu, Rewon Child, David Luan, Dario Amodei, and Ilya Sutskever. 2019. Language models are unsupervised multitask learners. *OpenAI blog*, 1(8):9.

Nils Reimers and Iryna Gurevych. 2019. Sentence-bert: Sentence embeddings using siamese bert-networks. In *Proceedings of the 2019 Conference on Empirical Methods in Natural Language Processing*. Association for Computational Linguistics.

Anna Rogers, Olga Kovaleva, and Anna Rumshisky. 2020. A primer in bertology: What we know about how bert works. *Transactions of the Association for Computational Linguistics*, 8:842–866.

Dhanasekar Sundararaman, Vivek Subramanian, Guoyin Wang, Shijing Si, Dinghan Shen, Dong Wang, and Lawrence Carin. 2019. Syntax-infused transformer and bert models for machine translation and natural language understanding. *arXiv preprint arXiv:1911.06156*.

Christian Szegedy, Vincent Vanhoucke, Sergey Ioffe, Jon Shlens, and Zbigniew Wojna. 2016. Rethinking the inception architecture for computer vision. In *Proceedings of the IEEE conference on computer vision and pattern recognition*, pages 2818–2826.

Jesse Vig. 2019. A multiscale visualization of attention in the transformer model. In *Proceedings of the 57th Annual Meeting of the Association for Computational Linguistics: System Demonstrations*, pages 37–42.

Jixuan Wang, Kai Wei, Martin Radfar, Weiwei Zhang, and Clement Chung. 2020a. Encoding syntactic knowledge in transformer encoder for intent detection and slot filling. *arXiv preprint arXiv:2012.11689*.

Wenhui Wang, Furu Wei, Li Dong, Hangbo Bao, Nan Yang, and Ming Zhou. 2020b. Minilm: Deep self-attention distillation for task-agnostic compression of pre-trained transformers. In *Advances in Neural Information Processing Systems*, volume 33, pages 5776–5788. Curran Associates, Inc.

Kilian Q Weinberger, John Blitzer, and Lawrence K Saul. 2005. Distance metric learning for large margin nearest neighbor classification. In *Proceedings of the 18th International Conference on Neural Information Processing Systems*, pages 1473–1480.

Thomas Wolf, Lysandre Debut, Victor Sanh, Julien Chaumond, Clement Delangue, Anthony Moi, Pierric Cistac, Tim Rault, Rémi Louf, Morgan Funtowicz, Joe Davison, Sam Shleifer, Patrick von Platen, Clara Ma, Yacine Jernite, Julien Plu, Canwen Xu, Teven Le Scao, Sylvain Gugger, Mariama Drame, Quentin Lhoest, and Alexander M. Rush. 2020. Transformers: State-of-the-art natural language processing. In *Proceedings of the 2020 Conference on Empirical Methods in Natural Language Processing: System Demonstrations*, pages 38–45, Online. Association for Computational Linguistics.

Zhilin Yang, Zihang Dai, Yiming Yang, Jaime Carbonell, Russ R Salakhutdinov, and Quoc V Le. 2019. Xlnet: Generalized autoregressive pretraining for language understanding. *Advances in Neural Information Processing Systems*, 32:5753–5763.

Manzil Zaheer, Guru Guruganesh, Kumar Avinava Dubey, Joshua Ainslie, Chris Alberti, Santiago Ontanon, Philip Pham, Anirudh Ravula, Qifan Wang, Li Yang, et al. 2020. Big bird: Transformers for longer sequences. *Advances in Neural Information Processing Systems*, 33.

Author Index

Association for Computational Linguistics
209 N. Eighth Street
Stroudsburg, Pennsylvania 18360

ISBN 978-1-7138-3389-5

9 781713 833895

CURRAN ASSOCIATES INC.
proceedings.com

Structures 2018

Transportation Research Record: Journal of the Transportation Research Board

Volume 2672, Issue 41

SAGE Publishing